Lattice Theory

LATTICE THEORY

by
HELMUTH GERICKE
Professor of Mathematics
University of Freiburg

FREDERICK UNGAR PUBLISHING CO.
NEW YORK

Originally published in German under the title
THEORIE DER VERBÄNDE

First published in Great Britain 1966
by GEORGE G. HARRAP & CO. LTD.
182 High Holborn, London, W.C.1

First American edition

Library of Congress No. 66-26204

Printed in Great Britain

Preface

Our object is to give an introduction, as elementary as possible, to Lattice Theory and also to the Theory of Relations. For pure lattice theory strictly speaking no special preliminary knowledge is required, but such applications of lattice theory as mathematical logic or the theory of groups cannot, of course, be presented in detail.

I have not aimed at completeness in the Bibliography and References, but I hope that I have mentioned the books in which readers can find references to further literature.

I should like to express my cordial thanks to Professor P. Lorenzen for many valuable suggestions and to Mr. Bammert for a careful reading of the manuscript.

My special thanks are due to the publishers for the loving care they have bestowed on the work and to the typesetters for their great patience in the often tedious task of setting the formulae.

Freiburg im Breisgau,
April 1963

GERICKE

Contents

INTRODUCTION

The Algebra of Logic

§ 1. Boolean algebra

One of the sources of Lattice Theory is the Algebra of Logic, the first systematic account of which was given by George Boole in 1847. Of course, some of the fundamental ideas go much further back. Let us have a look at Boole's later work, *An Investigation of the Laws of Thought*, 1854. Boole begins by developing a calculus of classes or sets. Small *italic* letters denote sets of objects; if x is the set of all sheep, y the set of all white objects, z the set of all horned objects, then xy is the set of all white sheep, and obviously

(1) $$xy = yx,$$

(2) $$xx = x.$$

xyz is the set of all horned white sheep, and obviously

(*) $$xyz = yzx = zxy = xzy = zyx = yxz.$$

The associative law

(3) $$x(yz) = (xy)z$$

has been tacitly assumed; together with (1) it suffices to prove (*).

Another combination of sets is illustrated by the example 'men and women'. If x is the set of men and y that of women, Boole writes $x+y$ for the set of men and women and observes that—'conventional notions apart'—'women and men' means the same thing, so that

(4) $$x+y = y+x.$$

The associative law

(5) $$x+(y+z) = (x+y)+z$$

is not mentioned explicitly. Boole illustrates the distributive law

(6) $$z(x+y) = zx+zy$$

by the example 'European men and women'.

Corresponding to addition, subtraction is introduced by writing $x=z-y$ when $x+y=z$. The concept of subtraction requires a more detailed discussion which we shall give later in a slightly different form. If 1 denotes the totality of all objects, then $1-x$ is called 'the complementary set to x'. By definition we have

(7) $$x+(1-x) = 1$$

and from (2) it follows that

$$x-x^2 = 0$$

(8) $$x(1-x) = 0$$

where 0 is the empty set, the set without any members.

In this way quite a number of rules of calculation have been formulated on which an 'algebra' can be built up. We shall treat some of this Boolean algebra in Chapter VI, § 3. In set theory we write $x \cap y$ instead of xy and $x \cup y$ instead of $x+y$.

Boolean algebra may also be applied to propositional calculus. For this application Boole interprets x as the time during which the proposition X is true, xy as the time in which the propositions X and Y are true simultaneously, and $x+y$ as the time in which X or Y are true. Finally, if 1 is the total interval of time in question, then $1-x$ is the time in which X is false. In this way the same calculus yields statements on the truth or falsity of combinations of propositions.

In the next section we develop propositional calculus from a different point of view. We shall return later to the calculus of sets.

§ 2. Classical propositional calculus (logic of connectives)

Propositional calculus was founded by the Stoics. Chrysippus (about 281–208 B.C.) gave the definition: *A proposition is what is true or false.* This means that the content of the proposition is ignored, and so is its construction from subject and predicate; attention is paid only to its *truth value*, True or False. Here we write 1 for 'True', 0 for 'False'.

There are combinations of propositions for which the truth value of the combined proposition depends only on the truth values of the constituents. Such combinations form the subject matter of propositional calculus. Some of them are familiar from everyday language and were investigated by the Stoics:

1) *Conjunction*: 'a and b', written $a \wedge b$, is defined as the proposition that is true if and only if a is true and b is true.

2) *Adjunction*: 'a or b', written $a \vee b$, is defined as the proposition that is true if a is true or b is true or both are true.

These combinations are therefore defined by prescribing their truth values for every possible choice of the truth values of a and b. This is illustrated in Table 1 (the last column will be explained later). We shall refer to it as 'Truth Table CL' (Truth Table of Classical Logic).

a	b	$a \wedge b$	$a \vee b$	$a \ulcorner\!- b$
0	0	0	0	1
0	1	0	1	1
1	0	0	1	0
1	1	1	1	1

TABLE 1. TRUTH TABLE CL

The common usage of the word 'or' is not unique. It can also be used to mean 'either a or b, but not both together'. Historically the name *disjunction* has been used for both combinations. We shall reserve it for the latter combination, and therefore (following Lorenzen) call the combination with the non-exclusive 'or' *adjunction*.

We call two composite propositions p and q *equivalent*, and write $p=q$ if they always have the same truth value (no matter how the values of 0 and 1 are distributed over their constituent propositions).

The *commutative laws*

(C1) $$a \wedge b = b \wedge a,$$

(C2) $$a \vee b = b \vee a,$$

are immediate consequences of the definitions.

From the verbal statement of the definitions of $\wedge$ and $\vee$ it might appear that there is nothing to prove; this is because the words 'and' and 'or' are used commutatively in everyday language. In fact, the table shows at a glance that when the values of a and b are interchanged, the values in the columns for $a \wedge b$ and $a \vee b$ do not change. (In the column for $a \ulcorner\!- b$ this is different.)

Next we have the *associative laws*:

(A1) $$a \wedge (b \wedge c) = (a \wedge b) \wedge c,$$

(A2) $$a \vee (b \vee c) = (a \vee b) \vee c.$$

These may be proved 'by substitution', namely by substituting all possible combinations of values for a, b, c. Table 2 shows that $a \wedge (b \wedge c)$ and $(a \wedge b) \wedge c$ always have the same truth value.

a	b	c	$b \wedge c$	$a \wedge (b \wedge c)$	$a \wedge b$	$(a \wedge b) \wedge c$
0	0	0	0	0	0	0
0	0	1	0	0	0	0
0	1	0	0	0	0	0
0	1	1	1	0	0	0
1	0	0	0	0	0	0
1	0	1	0	0	0	0
1	1	0	0	0	1	0
1	1	1	1	1	1	1

TABLE 2

In the same way one proves (A2), and also the *absorption laws*:

(Ab1) $$a \wedge (a \vee b) = a,$$

(Ab2) $$a \vee (a \wedge b) = b.$$

If in a set M two operations $\wedge$, $\vee$ *are defined for which the laws* (C), (A), (Ab) *hold, then* $(M, \wedge, \vee)$ *is called a dual group* (following Dedekind) *or a lattice.*

The truth table CL also yields the *distributive laws*:

(D1) $$a \wedge (b \vee c) = (a \wedge b) \vee (a \wedge c),$$

(D2) $$a \vee (b \wedge c) = (a \vee b) \wedge (a \vee c).$$

Again they are proved by substitution. A lattice in which they hold for any three elements is called a *distributive lattice.*

For every proposition a a *complement* a^0 can be defined by the truth table

a	0	1
a^0	1	0

(in words, 'not a' or 'non a'). With the help of Table 1 we see that $a \wedge a^0$ has the truth value 0 for every a. We denote such a proposition by n. If n_1 and n_2 are two such propositions that are 'always false', then $n_1 = n_2$. In this sense we speak of *the proposition n that is always false*. We also write

(C1) $$a \wedge a^0 = n.$$

This is the law of contradiction; a and non a cannot both be true simultaneously.

In the same way we denote by *e the proposition that is always true*. From the definition of a^0 by the truth table above we deduce:

(C2) $$a \vee a^0 = e.$$

This is the law of the excluded middle: at least one of the propositions a and non a is true.

Further, we have:

(N1) $a \wedge n = n$, (N2) $a \vee n = a$,

(E1) $a \wedge e = a$, (E2) $a \vee e = e$.

A lattice in which there are two elements n, e with the properties (N), (E) and for every element a there is an element a^0 with the properties (C1,2) is called a *complemented lattice*; a distributive complement lattice is called a *Boolean lattice*.

§ 3. Brouwer's propositional calculus

One assumption in the truth table CL is that every proposition is either true or false, a claim that is, to say the least, problematical for statements on infinite sets. L. E. J. Brouwer has defended the thesis (from 1907 on) that the law of the excluded middle is an inadmissible method of proof in mathematics. If one wants to formulate algebraically the logical rules admissible from his point of view, then one must choose another starting point in place of the truth table CL. One can start from *implication* as the fundamental concept. We introduce this concept first by means of the truth table CL, but later we shall free ourselves from this restriction.

Definition. We say that proposition a *implies* proposition b if b is true whenever a is true, and we write $a < b$.

This is not a combination of propositions, but a statement *about* the propositions a and b; it is a *meta-proposition.*

True, it is closely connected with a composite proposition, namely the *subjunction* $a \mathrel{\ulcorner\!-} b$ defined by the last column of Table 1: *a implies b precisely when $a \mathrel{\ulcorner\!-} b$ is true.*

To overcome the difficulty that, according to the definition, 'a implies b' does not say anything about b if a is false, we agree that a implies b when a is false whether b is true or false. This is not the place for a more detailed discussion.

For implication we have the rules:

(Br1) $a < a$ (clear from the definition);

(Br2) $a \wedge b < a,$ $a \wedge b < b;$

(Br3) $a < a \vee b,$ $b < a \vee b.$

Here we agree that $<$ separates more strongly than $\wedge, \vee, \mathrel{\ulcorner\!-}$. (Br2) and (Br3) can be read off Table 1.

When the validity of certain implications is known, we can deduce the validity of further implications.

(Br4) If $a < b$ and $b < c$, then $a < c$.

This can be deduced from the actual wording of the definition, but one can also verify by substitution that $a \mathrel{\ulcorner\!-} c$ is true if $a \mathrel{\ulcorner\!-} b$ and $b \mathrel{\ulcorner\!-} c$ are true.

For the phrase 'if..., then...' occurring in (Br4) we use the symbol $\Rightarrow$ and write (with a comma for 'and'):

(Br4) $a < b\,, b < c \Rightarrow a < c.$

Again by substitution we can prove:

(Br5) $c < a\,, c < b \Rightarrow c < a \wedge b;$

(Br6) $a < c\,, b < c \Rightarrow a \vee b < c.$

So we have two rules each for $\wedge$ and $\vee$ at our disposal, where $\wedge$ (or $\vee$, respectively) occurs once in the premise and once in the conclusion.

We note two rules about $\mathrel{\ulcorner\!-}$:

(Br7) $(a \wedge b) < c \Rightarrow a < (b \mathrel{\ulcorner\!-} c),$

(Br8) $a < (b \mathrel{\ulcorner\!-} c) \Rightarrow (a \wedge b) < c.$

They too can be proved by substitution, i.e. by showing that $(a \wedge b) \sqsubset c$ is true if and only if $a \sqsubset (b \sqsubset c)$ is true.

Now we can describe the new standpoint referred to above. We shall no longer use Chrysippus' definition of proposition. Instead, we must find some other way of defining what a proposition is. For example, one can state by what constructive prescriptions propositions may be formed. It will suffice for our purposes to know what a proposition is in the everyday usage of the term.

We renounce the tables of truth values, which contain the law of the excluded middle, and so renounce the definition of the symbols $\wedge, \vee, \sqsubset, <$ and the derivation of the rules (Br1 to 8). Instead, we start out from the rules (Br) themselves and regard them as prescriptions for working with the symbols mentioned. The only motivation we can give for these rules is as follows: they describe the common usage of the words 'and', 'or', 'if..., then...', 'implies'. For example, (Br7) is to be read: if the proposition 'a and b' implies the proposition c, then the proposition a alone implies the proposition 'if b, then c'. This is called the *rule of exportation*, because b is transported out of the premise. (Br8) is called the *rule of importation.* The validity of these rules can also be accepted as immediately obvious. A more exact foundation is possible, for example, on the basis of the operative interpretation of logic.

The logic built upon these rules is called Brouwer's positive logic of consequences. So far it does not contain negation. If we regard the rules only as rules of calculation, without thinking of the logical interpretation of the symbols, then we speak of *Brouwer's algebra.*

This algebra can be described in more detail: let M be a given set of objects and $<$ a relation between them. We assume, to begin with, that this relation satisfies (Br1) and (Br4). Next we assume: if $a<b$ and $b<a$, then $a=b$. This can be interpreted as a definition of $=$ (see Chapter I, § 2). We assume that for any two elements a and b of M there exists at least one element d with the property

(9) $$d < a, d < b$$

$$c < a, c < b \Rightarrow c < d \quad \text{(for all } c\text{)}$$

Then it follows immediately that there is only one element d of this kind. If there were two, d_1 and d_2, then it follows easily that $d_1 < d_2$ and $d_2 < d_1$ and so $d_1 = d_2$. This element is denoted by $d = a \wedge b$. It then satisfies (Br2) and (Br5).

Next we assume that for a and b there exists at least one element v with the properties

$$(10)\qquad a < v, b < v$$

$$a < w, b < w \Rightarrow v < w \quad \text{(for all } w\text{)}$$

Then there is only one such element v; we denote it by $a \vee b$. It satisfies (Br3) and (Br6).

Now it can be shown that the commutative, associative, and absorption laws hold. For example, we have

	$b \wedge a < a$	by (Br2),
	$b \wedge a < b$	by (Br2),
hence	$b \wedge a < a \wedge b$	by (Br5).

In the same way we prove $a \wedge b < b \wedge a$.
As a further example we prove (Ab1)

1)	$a \wedge (a \vee b) < a$	by (Br2),
2)	$a < a$	by (Br1),
	$a < a \vee b$	by (Br3),
hence	$a < a \wedge (a \vee b)$	by (Br2).

The remaining proofs are left to the reader.

So we have shown that M, with the relation $<$ and the combinations $\wedge$, $\vee$ defined by it, forms a lattice.

For any two elements a and b in a lattice there is at most one element c with the property that for all x

$$(11)\qquad x \wedge a < b \Rightarrow x < c \quad \text{and} \quad x < c \Rightarrow x \wedge a < b$$

are true. For if there were a second element d such that for all x

$$(12)\qquad x \wedge a < b \Rightarrow x < d \quad \text{and} \quad x < d \Rightarrow x \wedge a < b,$$

then it would follow from the second part of (11) with $x = c$ that

$$c \wedge a < b$$

and so from the first part of (12): $c < d$.

From the second part of (12) and the first part of (11) it follows that $d < c$; hence $d = c$.

If for any two elements a and b in a lattice there is one—and hence only one—element c with the property (11), then we denote it by $a \sqsubset b$ and call the lattice a *Brouwer lattice* or *subjunctive lattice*.

Having introduced the name 'lattice' we shall now use it in place of Brouwer algebra. By definition (Br7) and (Br8) hold.

An important theorem is: *every Brouwer lattice is distributive.*

Here we prove that

$$a \wedge (b \vee c) < (a \wedge b) \vee (a \wedge c).$$

In Chapter VI, § 1 we shall show that the distributive laws are then satisfied.

As an abbreviation we write $(a \wedge b) \vee (a \wedge c) = p$.

Then we have
1. $a \wedge b < p$ by (Br3),
2. $a \wedge c < p$ by (Br3),
3. $b < (a \sqsubset p)$ by line 1 and (C1), (Br7),
4. $c < (a \sqsubset p)$ by line 2 and (C1), (Br7),
5. $b \vee c < (a \sqsubset p)$ by (Br6),
6. $a \wedge (b \vee c) < p$ by (Br8).

Brouwer lattices will be treated in Chapter VI, § 2.

§ 4. Explanation of symbols frequently used

The introduction was meant to show that the process of algebraization of logic leads to lattices. Now we shall develop the algebra of lattices, irrespective of the fact that part of this theory can be interpreted as the algebra of logic. In this algebra of lattices we speak of

elements a, b... of a set M or V (which *can* be propositions in applications to the algebra of logic);

combinations denoted by $\sqcap$, $\sqcup$ (which *can* be the combinations of propositions $\wedge$, $\vee$ in applications to logic); also subjunction $\sqsubset$ will appear in this role in Chapter VI, § 2;

an order relation $\leqslant$ (which *can* be the implication $<$);

the complement a^0 (which *can* be the negation $\neg a$).

But in addition combinations of propositions will continue to occur explicitly as combinations of statements *about* the elements of the set or the lattice, respectively. For this purpose we shall now use the symbols

$\wedge$ and	$\vee$ or
$\rightarrow$ if..., then	$\leftrightarrow$ if and only if

Note. In most cases $\rightarrow$ is to be interpreted as subjunction. However, for our applications the difference between the statement 'A $\rightarrow$ B'

(when **A** and **B** are propositions) and the meta-statement '**A** → **B** is true' is essential.

Finally, we denote by

$\neg$ non, not,

$\bigwedge_{x}$ for all x,

$\bigwedge_{x \in M}$ for all x in the set M,

$\bigvee_{x}$ there is an x with the property...; or: for at least one x,

$\bigvee_{x \in M}$ for at least one x in the set M,

$\leftrightharpoons$ this symbol denotes a definition and is to be read according to the context in which it stands as 'equal' or 'if and only if'.

CHAPTER I

Sets and Relations

§ 1. Explanation of the fundamental concepts

We assume that the reader is familiar with the concept 'set' and that he is conversant with the meaning of the statement 'x is an element of the set M'; as usual we write

$$x \in M.$$

One often says that a set is characterized by a property (which is shared precisely by its elements). In this context we need the concept of 'predicate.' The formula $x+3=4$ for instance has (verbally) the form of a proposition; but it would be meaningless to ask whether it is true or false, as long as no provision is made for the variable x. Of course, first of all it must be stated what kind of objects may be substituted for x; in our case, for example, natural numbers. Even then one can make various dispositions about x:

1. by 'binding' the variable, for example by the *quantifiers* $\bigwedge_x$ (for all admissible x), $\bigvee_x$ (there is an x), that is, either $\bigwedge_x (x+3=4)$—this proposition is false—, or $\bigvee_x (x+3=4)$—this proposition is true;

2. by substituting for the variables admissible elements from their range of variability; in our case, a natural number for x.

A formula that contains free, i.e. not bound, variables and becomes a proposition if the variables are replaced by elements from the ranges of variability is called a *predicate*.

We shall need a few of the rules of the logic of quantifiers, which we give here without going into the details of their justification. If the reader thinks of their meaning, he will accept them as valid.

(Q1) $$\bigwedge_x \bigwedge_y A(x,y) \leftrightarrow \bigwedge_y \bigwedge_x A(x,y)$$

(Q2) $$\bigvee_x \bigvee_y A(x,y) \leftrightarrow \bigvee_y \bigvee_x A(x,y)$$

(Q3) $$C \wedge \bigvee_x B(x) \leftrightarrow \bigvee_x (C \wedge B(x))$$

provided the variable x does not occur freely in C.

This is a generalization of the distributive law; if x can take only the values 1 or 2, then (Q3) becomes

$$A \wedge (B_1 \vee B_2) \leftrightarrow (A \wedge B_1) \vee (A \wedge B_2).$$

(Q4) $$\bigwedge_x (A(x) \rightarrow B) \leftrightarrow \bigvee_x (A(x)) \rightarrow B.$$

If x can take only the values 1 or 2, this becomes

$$(A_1 \rightarrow B) \wedge (A_2 \rightarrow B) \leftrightarrow (A_1 \vee A_2) \rightarrow B.$$

This can be checked, for example, by means of the Truth Table CL (page 13), or can be translated into the equation

$$(A_1^0 \vee B) \wedge (A_2^0 \vee B) = (A_1 \vee A_2)^0 \vee B$$

which can be verified in accordance with the rules of a Boolean lattice.

If $A(x)$ is a predicate containing the free variable x, then we denote by

$$\{x;\, A(x)\}$$

the set of all x for which $A(x)$ is true, i.e.

$$y \in \{x;\, A(x)\} \leftrightharpoons A(y).$$

Quite generally we use curly brackets to denote the elements of a set; for example, if $A(x)$ is the predicate $x \leqslant 4$ for natural numbers x, then we write

$$\{x;\, A(x)\} = \{x;\, x \leqslant 4\} = \{1, 2, 3, 4\}.$$

The sequence in which the elements of a set are given is immaterial.

N is called a *subset* of M, in symbols $N \subseteq M$, if for all x the statement $x \in N$ implies the statement $x \in M$:

$$N \subseteq M \leftrightharpoons \bigwedge_x (x \in N \rightarrow x \in M).$$

The subsets of a set M are the elements of the *power set* $\mathfrak{P}M$.

The *intersection* of two sets A and B is defined by

$$A \cap B \leftrightharpoons \{x;\, x \in A \wedge x \in B\},$$

i.e. $$x \in A \cap B \leftrightharpoons x \in A \wedge x \in B.$$

The *union* of A and B is defined by

$$A \cup B \leftrightharpoons \{x;\, x \in A \vee x \in B\},$$

i.e.

$$x \in A \cup B \leftrightharpoons x \in A \vee x \in B.$$

The intersection of an arbitrary number of sets is defined as follows: let $\mathfrak{M}$ be a set of subsets of M, so that $\mathfrak{M} \subseteq \mathfrak{P}M$. Then we write

$$\bigcap_{X \in \mathfrak{M}} X = \bigcap_{\mathfrak{M}} X \leftrightharpoons \{a;\, \bigwedge_{X \in \mathfrak{M}} a \in X\},$$

i.e.

$$a \in \bigcap_{X \in \mathfrak{M}} X \leftrightharpoons \bigwedge_{X \in \mathfrak{M}} a \in X.$$

Correspondingly the union is defined as follows:

$$\bigcup_{X \in \mathfrak{M}} X = \bigcup_{\mathfrak{M}} X \leftrightharpoons \{a;\, \bigvee_{X \in \mathfrak{M}} a \in X\}.$$

The set of pairs (x_1, x_2) of elements of two sets M_1, M_2 is called the *cartesian product*:

$$M_1 \times M_2 = \{(x_1, x_2);\, x_1 \in M_1, x_2 \in M_2\}.$$

The pairs (x_1, x_2) and (x_2, x_1) are to be regarded as distinct. The sets M_1, M_2 need not be distinct. For example, if $M_1 = M_2 = M$ is the set of real numbers x with $0 \leqslant x \leqslant 1$, then $M \times M$ can be regarded as the set of points of the square in Fig. 1.

By a corresponding definition:

$$M_1 \times M_2 \times \ldots \times M_k = \{(x_1, x_2, \ldots, x_k);\, x_\kappa \in M_\kappa \text{ for all } \kappa = 1, 2, \ldots, k\}.$$

A predicate $A(x_1, \ldots, x_k)$ with k variables and the domains of variability $x_1 \in M_1, \ldots, x_k \in M_k$ defines a subset of $M_1 \times \ldots \times M_k$, namely the set R_A, as all k-tuples for which $A(x_1, \ldots, x_k)$ holds:

$$R_A = \{(x_1, \ldots, x_k);\, A(x_1, \ldots, x_k)\}$$

or

$$(x_1, \ldots, x_k) \in R_A \leftrightarrow A(x_1, \ldots, x_k).$$

R_A is called the *extent* of A or the *relation* defined by A.

Since every set is defined by a predicate (see above, page 21), *every* subset of $M_1 \times \ldots \times M_k$ is a k-ary relation.

$R_A \subseteq R_B$ holds if and only if

$$\bigwedge_{x_1} \ldots \bigwedge_{x_k} (A(x_1, \ldots, x_k) \rightarrow B(x_1, \ldots, x_k))$$

we also say: R_A *implies* R_B.

$R_A = R_B$ holds if and only if

$$\bigwedge_{x_1} .. \bigwedge_{x_k} (A(x_1,\ldots,x_k) \leftrightarrow B(x_1,\ldots,x_k)).$$

All predicates of the same extent as A define the same relation. Nevertheless in most cases we shall use the same letter for a relation and the predicate defining it, and occasionally we shall refer to the predicate A itself as 'the relation A'.

§ 2. Binary relation on a set M

A binary relation R is a subset of the cartesian product $R \subseteq M \times M$.

If the relation R holds for the pair (x,y), then we write $(x,y) \in R$ or xRy. It is useful to picture binary relations in a concrete fashion as subsets of the square in Fig. 1, for example the relation $x \leqslant y$ as the shaded triangle in Fig. 2.

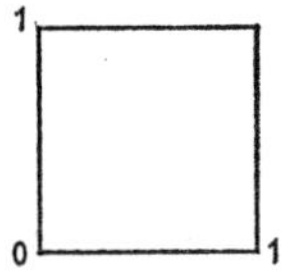

Fig. 1

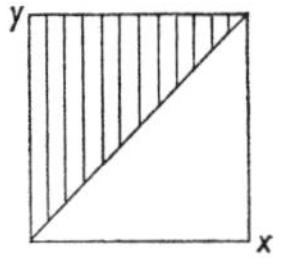

Fig. 2

A few special relations are:

$xUy \leftrightarrows (x,y) \in M \times M$, i.e. the relation that holds for all pairs (x,y), the all-relation;

$x \varnothing y$, the null-relation which holds for no pair (x,y);

$xDy \leftrightarrows x = y$, the relation of equality which is represented in the figure by the diagonal of the square. If several sets have to be considered, equality in the set M is denoted by D_M.

Every subset of $M \times M$ is a relation (the additional word 'binary' will be omitted in this section). Our task is to select from this wealth of material some relations that are mathematically useful. This can be understood, for example, as relations that enable us to make deductions about the existence of further relations, just as from $x = y$ and $y = z$ we can infer that $x = z$.

This problem engaged Aristotle's attention. He considered several relations between sets s and p (traditionally, subject and predicate):

sAp: all s are p; in other words, all elements of s are also elements of p;

sEp: no s is p;

sIp: some s are p;

sOp: some s are not p.

If two such relations hold, then the fact that a third one holds can be deduced, if at all, only if there is a common middle term m. For example,

I	$sAm \wedge mAp \rightarrow sAp$;
II	$sAm \wedge pEm \rightarrow sEp$;
III	$mAs \wedge mIp \rightarrow sIp$;
IV	$mAs \wedge pEm \rightarrow sOp$.

One way of making the validity of these 'syllogisms' evident is to draw s, m, p as point sets in the plane. Example IV is illustrated by Figs. 3a or 3b. Some elements of s, namely those of m, are not elements of p.

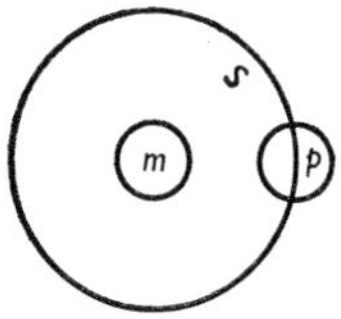

Fig. 3a

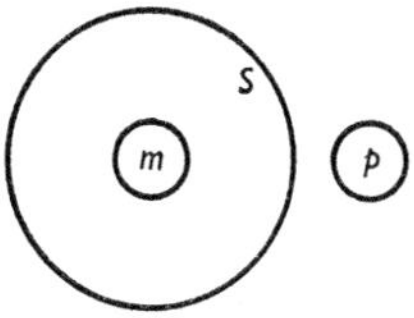

Fig. 3b

The four examples show that the middle term can stand in different places. This yields the four 'figures of the syllogism'.

We now pose the question somewhat differently; we only consider one relation R and ask what can be deduced when R has one of the following four properties:

I	$xRy \wedge yRz \rightarrow xRz$	(Transitivity)
II	$xRy \wedge zRy \rightarrow xRz$	(Right comparability)
III	$yRx \wedge yRz \rightarrow xRz$	(Left comparability)
IV	$yRx \wedge zRy \rightarrow xRz$.	

Relations with property I are called *transitive*.

II and III are generalizations of Euclid's axiom: if two quantities are equal to a third, then they are equal to each other. For this reason relations with these properties are called *right*- or *left-comparable*, respectively.

IV can be satisfied by a cyclic arrangement of points on a circle (see below, page 29).

It is convenient and involves no essential loss of generality to assume that for every x there is a y with xRy; in symbols

V $$\bigwedge_x \bigvee_y xRy.$$

A relation with this property will be called *left total.*

In particular, a relation is left total (and right total) if

VI $$\bigwedge_x xRx$$

holds. It is then called *reflexive.*

The properties I–VI are not independent of each other. In a certain sense comparability II (and similarly III) is strongest. We prove:

1) II and V imply VI.

Proof. If x is given, we choose a y with xRy. Then we have $xRy \wedge xRy$, and so by II, xRx.

1a) Similarly VI follows from III and right totality $\bigwedge_x \bigvee_y yRx$.

2) II and VI imply *symmetry*

VII $$xRy \to yRx.$$

Proof. $xRy \to yRy \wedge xRy \to yRx$.

2a) Similarly symmetry follows from III and VI.

3) From II and VII (and also from III and VII) follow I, III (II, respectively), and IV.

We repeat: from II and V follow VI, VII, and I. Conversely it is easy to see that from VI, I, and VII follow II and V. Relations having these properties are called *equivalence relations.*

Example. Two sets a and b are called equal if they consist of the same elements: in symbols

(1) $$a = b \leftrightharpoons \bigwedge_\xi (\xi \in a \leftrightarrow \xi \in b)$$

We leave it to the reader to verify that the relation so defined has the properties of an equivalence. A comparison of (1) and the definition of $\subseteq$ (page 22) shows that

$$a = b \leftrightarrow a \subseteq b \wedge b \subseteq a.$$

An equivalence relation A makes it possible to partition M into 'equivalence classes'. We can define

$$Kx = \{y; yAx\}, \text{ in other words: } y \in Kx \leftrightarrow yAx.$$

This partition into classes has the following characteristics:

1) Every $x \in M$ belongs to at least one class. For on account of reflexivity we have xAx, hence $x \in Kx$.

2) Every $x \in M$ belongs to at most one class. In other words, if two classes Ky and Kz have an element x in common, then $Ky = Kz$, i.e. Ky and Kz have all their elements in common.

Proof. The assumptions state: xAy and xAz. The claim is: $\bigwedge_w wAy \leftrightarrow wAz$.

From xAy and xAz and wAy it follows, in fact, that wAz.
From xAy and xAz and wAz it follows that wAy.

3) Similarly one can prove:

$$Kx = Ky \leftrightarrow xAy.$$

The equivalence of elements corresponds to the equality of classes.

Example. For complex numbers α, β the relation $\alpha A \beta \leftrightharpoons |\alpha| = |\beta|$ is an equivalence. Equivalence classes in the complex plane are circles around the origin.

Transitivity I and left totality V do not imply symmetry.

Example. The set of natural numbers with the relation $\leqslant$.

Relations with properties I and V could be called order relations in the widest sense. But it is customary to define an order relation by further restrictive conditions.

It is not essential to postulate reflexivity. For with every transitive left total relation R we can associate a relation R^* which coincides with R for $x \neq y$, is also left total and transitive, but in addition reflexive:

$$xR^*y \leftrightharpoons xRy \vee x = y.$$

The symbol '=' here denotes identity, the most important property of which is that every true statement in which x occurs remains true if x is replaced by a y with $x = y$. In symbols,

$$\text{(G)} \qquad x = y \wedge A(x) \rightarrow A(y).$$

A left total relation with this property is an equivalence, for if we apply (G) to $A(x) \leftrightharpoons x = y$, then we obtain

$$x = y \wedge x = y \rightarrow y = y;$$

now left totality implies reflexivity. If we apply (G) to $A(x) \leftrightharpoons x = z$, then we obtain

$$x = y \wedge x = z \rightarrow y = z,$$

i.e. left comparability.

This is needed to prove that R^* is transitive. Suppose that

$$xR^*y, \text{ i.e. } xRy \vee x = y$$

and

$$yR^*z, \text{ i.e. } yRz \vee y = z.$$

If xRy and yRz hold, then it follows from the transitivity of R that xRz, i.e. xR^*z.

If xRy and $y = z$ hold, then xRz follows from (G) applied to $y = z$ and $A(y) = xRy$.

If $x = y$ and yRz hold, then xRz follows correspondingly.

If $x = y$ and $y = z$ hold, then $x = z$ follows from the transitivity of '='. (The point is to find out precisely what individual logical steps are made in these very simple proofs.)

That the left totality of R^* follows from that of R is clear. Riguet called R^* *the reflexive hull* (fermeture réflexive) of R. Conversely, one can associate with a reflexive relation R^* one that is not reflexive:

$$xRy \leftrightharpoons xR^*y \wedge x \neq y.$$

A reflexive and transitive relation is called a *quasi-order*.

If the relation $\leqslant$ is a quasi-order and in addition *anti-symmetric*, i.e.

$$x \leqslant y \wedge y \leqslant x \rightarrow x = y,$$

then it is called an *order* (or *order relation* or partial order or semi-order). If in addition

$$\bigwedge_x \bigwedge_y (x \leqslant y \vee y \leqslant x),$$

then we speak of a *linear order* (or total order or just order, in case the preceding relation is called partial order). We shall keep to the names given in italics.

We use the symbol $\leqslant$ quite generally for a quasi-order or (in most cases) an order. The relation 'less than or equal' for real numbers will be denoted, if necessary, by $\underset{z}{\leqslant}$.

Examples. 1) The all-relation U is a quasi-order.

2) In the set of complex numbers let a be fixed. We define

$x \mathrel{\dot{\leqslant}} y$ as meaning 'the distance of x from a is greater than or equal to that of y', i.e.

$$x \mathrel{\dot{\leqslant}} y \leftrightharpoons |x-a| \underset{z}{\geqslant} |y-a|.$$

This relation is a quasi-order; but it is not anti-symmetric. In the set of equivalence classes under the relation A:

$$xAy \leftrightharpoons x \mathrel{\dot{\leqslant}} y \wedge y \mathrel{\dot{\leqslant}} x, \text{i.e. } |x-a| = |y-a|.$$

To the quasi-order $\dot{\leqslant}$ there corresponds an order $\leqslant$:

$$Kx \leqslant Ky \leftrightharpoons x \mathrel{\dot{\leqslant}} y.$$

As in example 2), one can pass from every quasi-order $\dot{\leqslant}$ to an order by defining a relation $\equiv$ as follows:

$$x \equiv y \leftrightharpoons x \mathrel{\dot{\leqslant}} y \wedge y \mathrel{\dot{\leqslant}} x.$$

It can be verified immediately that this is an equivalence relation. In the set of equivalence classes an order is defined by

$$Kx \leqslant Ky \leftrightharpoons x \mathrel{\dot{\leqslant}} y.$$

We leave it to the reader to prove that this is, in fact, an order. (One has to show first of all that the definition of $Kx \leqslant Ky$ does not depend on the representatives chosen, i.e.

$$Kx \leqslant Ky \wedge Kx = Kz \rightarrow Kz \leqslant Ky.)$$

Property IV does not appear to play an important role in mathematics. In the following sense it is stronger than I. IV and reflexivity imply symmetry, for from $yRx \wedge yRy$ it follows by IV that xRy. So we again have an equivalence.

However, there are relations that satisfy IV and V, but are not reflexive. For example: let M consist of the three elements a, b, c; let R be defined as the set of pairs (a,b), (b,c), (c,a) i.e. aRb, bRc, cRa. This relation is right and left total and transitive, but not reflexive.

§ 3. Operations

The properties of relations discussed so far enable us to infer from the validity of the relation for two pairs of arguments the validity for a third pair. Another method of inference occurs if in a $(k+1)$-ary relation the first k arguments determine the $(k+1)$st in the sense that

$R(x_1,\ldots,x_k,u)$ has the property that for every k-tuple $x_1 \in M_1,\ldots,$ $x_k \in M_k$ there is at most one $u \in M$ such that R holds:

(E) $\bigwedge\limits_{x_1 \in M_1} \ldots \bigwedge\limits_{x_k \in M_k} \bigwedge\limits_{u \in M} \bigwedge\limits_{v \in M} (R(x_1,\ldots,x_k,u) \wedge R(x_1,\ldots,x_k,v) \rightarrow u = v).$

If the number of arguments is clear, we write as an abbreviation

$$(x_1,\ldots,x_k) = \mathfrak{x},$$

$$M_1 \times \ldots \times M_k = \prod_{\kappa=1}^{k} M_\kappa = \prod M_k = P.$$

Then (E) takes the form:

(E) $$\bigwedge_{\kappa \in \Pi M \mathfrak{x}} \bigwedge_{u \in M} \bigwedge_{v \in M} (R(\mathfrak{x},u) \wedge R(\mathfrak{x},v) \rightarrow u = v).$$

A relation with this property is called a *mapping from* the set $P = \prod M_\kappa$ *into* the set M (also for an arbitrary set P). The sets $M_1,\ldots,M_k, M$ need not be distinct. The element u uniquely determined by $R(\mathfrak{x},u)$ is called the *image* of $(x_1,\ldots,x_k)=\mathfrak{x}$ and is denoted by

$$u = f_R(x_1,\ldots,x_k) = f_R\mathfrak{x}$$

(without brackets in the case of a single argument). If there is no need to refer to the relation R explicitly, we write $u=f(x_1,\ldots,x_k)=f_\mathfrak{x}$. We also talk of the *mapping* f or the *function* f. For a mapping we use the symbol $\rightarrowtail$, both for sets ($P \rightarrowtail M$) as well as for the individual elements ($\mathfrak{x} \rightarrowtail u = f_\mathfrak{x}$).

If every element of P has an image in M, i.e. if

(T) $$\bigwedge_{\mathfrak{x} \in P} \bigvee_{u \in M} R(\mathfrak{x},u),$$

in other words, if R is left total, then R is called a mapping *of* P into M. Mappings with this property are also called *operations* (for details see below). If every element of M is the image of an element of P, i.e. if

$$\bigwedge_{u \in M} \bigvee_{\mathfrak{x} \in P} R(\mathfrak{x},u),$$

then R is called a mapping from P *onto* M.

A $(k+1)$-ary relation satisfying (E) and (T) is called a k-ary *operation*, specifically an *inner operation* of M if $M_1=\ldots=M_k=M$. Examples of binary operations are addition, subtraction, multiplication, division, exponentiation of numbers, intersection and union of sets, conjunction, adjunction, and subjunction of propositions.

Following Bourbaki, one uses the symbol $\top$ as a general symbol for a binary inner operation, i.e. a mapping of $M \times M$ into M, and writes $x_1 \top x_2 = y$.

Scalar multiplication of vectors by numbers ($\lambda \mathfrak{x} = \mathfrak{y}$) is an example of an *external operation*; here M_1 is the set of real numbers, $M_2 = M$ the set of vectors. In a binary external operation one occasionally calls $M_1 = \Omega$ the *operator domain* and, again following Bourbaki, denotes the mapping of $\Omega \times M$ into M by $\omega \perp x = y$. An external operation can also be characterized as follows: a mapping of M into M is associated with every ω in Ω.

If a finite collection of relations $(R_1, \ldots, R_m)$ in a set is given, then $(M; R_1, \ldots, R_m)$ is called a *formation* or a *relative*. If all the *defining relations* of a formation are operations, then $(M; R_1, \ldots, R_m)$ is called an *operational formation*. For convenience we assume that the R_i are internal operations; only on occasion shall we point out what additional arguments are required when external operations are present. To begin with we would have to assume that for every external operation R_i an operation domain Ω_i is given.

§ 4. Operations on binary relations

4.1. *The relation product*

In the syllogisms we came across a combination of binary relations. If R, S, T are variables for which the relations A, E, I, O (see page 24) may be substituted, then a syllogism of the first figure has the form

$$sRm \wedge mSp \rightarrow sTp.$$

Definition. Let $R \subseteq M_1 \times M_2$, $S \subseteq M_2 \times M_3$. The relation $RS \subseteq M_1 \times M_3$ defined by

(1) $$xRSy \Leftrightarrow \bigvee_{z \in M_2} (xRz \wedge zSy)$$

is called the *product* of the relations R and S.

As a rule, the product is formed only in the case $M_1 = M_2 = M_3 = M$. Therefore we assume here:

$$R, S, T, \ldots \subseteq M \times M.$$

The relation product satisfies the associative law

(2) $$(RS)T = R(ST).$$

Proof.

$$x(RS)Ty \text{ states that } \bigvee_w (\bigvee_z (xRz \wedge zSw) \wedge wTy).$$

$$xR(ST)y \text{ states that } \bigvee_z (xRz \wedge \bigvee_w (zSw \wedge wTy)).$$

To verify that these predicates are logically equivalent, one needs the rules (Q2), (Q3) of § 1. The proof is left to the reader.

There is a *neutral element* for the multiplication of relations, namely the relation D defined by $xDy \leftrightharpoons x=y$. It is easy to verify that

$$RD = DR = R.$$

If R and S are mappings of a set M into itself, then z in (1) is uniquely determined by x and y by z, hence also uniquely determined by x, hence RS is again a mapping. We have

$$z = f_R(x),\ y = f_S(z) = f_S(f_R(x)).$$

We can write: $f_{RS}=f_S f_R$. The (relation) product of two mappings is the result of carrying them out in succession. It is a frequently used theorem that the successive application of mappings is always associative. That is the reason why we have treated the logical foundation of the proof in so much detail.

4.2. The inverse relation. Presentation of properties of relations

The relation $\tilde{R}$ defined by $y\tilde{R}x \leftrightharpoons xRy$ is called the *inverse* relation to R. Obviously,

$$\tilde{\tilde{R}} = R,\ \tilde{D} = D.$$

By means of multiplication and inversion of relations the properties of binary relations can be written in a new form.

To begin with, let $R \subseteq M \times M$.

1) R is *reflexive*: $x=y \to xRy$, i.e. $D \subseteq R$.
2) R is *transitive*: $\bigwedge_x \bigwedge_y \bigwedge_z (xRy \wedge yRz \to xRz)$.

On account of (Q1) and (Q4) (§ 1) this is equivalent to

$$\bigwedge_x \bigwedge_z (\bigvee_y (xRy \wedge yRz) \to xRz),$$

i.e. R is transitive if $RR \subseteq R$.

In what follows we do not write down the $\bigwedge$-quantifiers.

3) R is *right comparable*: $xRy \wedge zRy \to xRz$,

i.e. $$xRy \wedge y\tilde{R}z \to xRz, \text{ i.e. } R\tilde{R} \subseteq R.$$

4) R is *left comparable*: $yRx \wedge yRz \to xRz$, i.e. $\tilde{R}R \subseteq R$.

5) R is *symmetrical*: $xRy \to yRx$, i.e. $R = \tilde{R}$.

Now, more generally, let $R \subseteq M \times N$.

6) R is a mapping from M into N if (see § 3)

$$\bigwedge_{x \in M} \bigwedge_{y \in N} \bigwedge_{z \in N} (xRy \wedge xRz \to y = z),$$

i.e. by (Q4) if

$$\bigwedge_{y \in N} \bigwedge_{z \in N} (\bigvee_{x \in M} (y\tilde{R}x \wedge xRz) \to y = z), \text{ i.e. } \tilde{R}R \subseteq D_N.$$

R is a mapping from N into M if $R\tilde{R} \subseteq D_M$.

If R and $\tilde{R}$ are mappings, in other words if

$$\tilde{R}R \subseteq D_N \wedge R\tilde{R} \subseteq D_M,$$

then R is called *invertible* or *bi-unique*. If R is an invertible mapping, $xRy \leftrightarrow y = f_R(x)$, then for $y\tilde{R}x$ (i.e. xRy) we also write $x = f_{\tilde{R}}^{-1}(y)$. f^{-1} is called the *inverse* mapping.

7) We ask: what is the meaning of $D_M \subseteq R\tilde{R}$?

$$\bigwedge_{x \in M} \bigwedge_{y \in M} (x = y \to \bigvee_{z \in N} (xRz \wedge z\tilde{R}y)),$$

i.e. $\bigwedge_{x \in M} \bigvee_{z \in N} (xRz \wedge z\tilde{R}x)$, i.e. $\bigwedge_{x \in M} \bigvee_{z \in N} xRz$, i.e. R is *left total*. In that case $\tilde{R}$ is *right total*.

8) R is a mapping *of* M into N if R is left total. Such a mapping is then characterized by

$$\tilde{R}R \subseteq D_N \wedge D_M \subseteq R\tilde{R}.$$

R is a mapping of M *onto* N if

$$\tilde{R}R \subseteq D_N \wedge D_N \subseteq R\tilde{R}.$$

R is an invertible mapping *of* M *onto* N if

$$\tilde{R}R = D_N \wedge D_M = R\tilde{R}.$$

If $M = N$, we omit the suffix in D and so obtain as a characterization of an invertible mapping of a set M into itself:

$$R\tilde{R} = \tilde{R}R = D.$$

A map with a binary operation is called a *group* if the operation is associative, if there is a neutral element, and if for each element there exists an inverse.

Therefore a set Φ of mappings of a set M onto itself forms a group under the operation of successive application if it contains the '*identity mapping*' D ($f_D(x)=x$), if every mapping $f \in \Phi$ is invertible and f^{-1} belongs to Φ. Associativity was proved above quite generally. The train of thought begun here will be resumed later. But first we shall investigate sets with order relations (in the widest sense).

CHAPTER II

Quasi-ordered and Ordered Sets

§ 1. Generalities

1.1. Definitions (revision)

The relation $\leqslant$ in a set M is a *quasi-order* if it satisfies the axioms

(r) $$\bigwedge_x x \leqslant x \qquad \text{(reflexivity)}$$

(t) $$x \leqslant y \wedge y \leqslant z \rightarrow x \leqslant z \quad \text{(transitivity)}$$

$(M, \leqslant)$ is then called a *quasi-ordered set.*

If $(M, \leqslant)$ is a quasi-ordered set and if

(as) $$x \leqslant y \wedge y \leqslant x \rightarrow x = y \quad \text{(anti-symmetry)},$$

then $\leqslant$ is called an *order* or *order relation,* and $(M, \leqslant)$ is called an *ordered set.*

If in addition

(l) $$\bigwedge_x \bigwedge_y x \leqslant y \vee y \leqslant x,$$

then $(M, \leqslant)$ is called a *linearly ordered set* or *chain.*

1.2. Examples (see also Chapter I, § 2)

1) For propositions implication, denoted by $<$ in Intro. § 3, is a quasi-order on account of (Br1) and (Br4). If one defines, as usual, equivalence of propositions by

$$a < b \text{ and } b < a,$$

then one obtains an order relation for the classes of equivalent propositions. (Compare Chapter I, § 2.)

2) For the set $\mathfrak{P}e$ of subsets of a set e inclusion ('being contained') $\subseteq$ is an order relation. $(\mathfrak{P}e, \subseteq)$ is an ordered set.

We obtain further examples with the help of the following

> *Theorem.* If $(M, \leqslant)$ is an ordered set, N a subset of M, and if we define in N a relation R by $xRy \leftrightharpoons x \leqslant y$, then R is an order relation on N. Of course, we also denote it by $\leqslant$.

2a) If e is a group, Ue the set of all subgroups of e, then $(Ue, \subseteq)$ is an ordered set. Similarly for rings, fields, etc.

3) The set of natural numbers (excluding 0) is denoted by $\boldsymbol{N}$. Let $a|b$ mean 'a is a divisor of b'; then $(\boldsymbol{N}, |)$ is an ordered set.

4) Let $\underset{z}{\leqslant}$ mean 'less than or equal to' for real numbers. If $\boldsymbol{Q}$ is the set of rational numbers, $\boldsymbol{R}$ the set of real numbers, then $(\boldsymbol{N}, \underset{z}{\leqslant})$, $(\boldsymbol{Q}, \underset{z}{\leqslant})$, $(\boldsymbol{R}, \underset{z}{\leqslant})$ are linearly ordered sets.

1.3. Order diagrams

If an ordered set consists of a finite number of elements, then the order can be illustrated by an *order diagram* or Hasse diagram. To describe it we define: a is called a *lower neighbour* of b if

$$a < b$$
$$\bigwedge_x (a \leqslant x \leqslant b \rightarrow x = a \vee x = b),$$

(i.e. if no element of M lies 'between' a and b). Now we can represent every element of M by a small circle and join neighbouring elements, which have to be arranged so that b stands higher than a if a is a lower neighbour of b. For ordered sets of three elements we have the following possibilities:

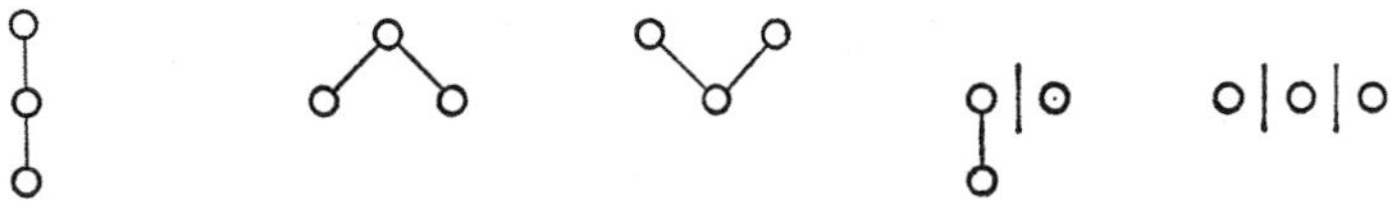

Fig. 4a

for four elements among others:

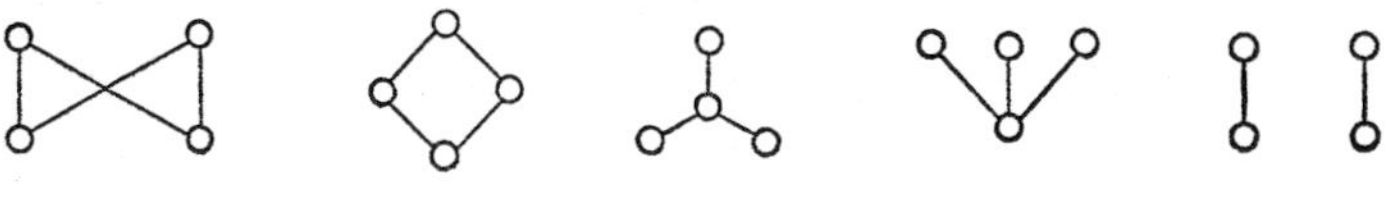

Fig. 4b

The last example shows that an ordered set can split into ordered subsets that are not connected at all with each other.

It would be tedious to give a *precise* description of the order diagram; we can omit this, because we wish to use it only for the purpose of illustration and not for proofs.

The fact that certain properties of infinite ordered or even quasi-ordered sets can be illustrated similarly will be used on occasion.

§ 2. Bounds and limits

2.1. Definitions

In the following definitions we shall not ask, to begin with, whether the defined sets or elements exist.

Let $(M, \leqslant)$ be a quasi-ordered set and $N \subseteq M$. t is called an *upper bound* for N, if $\bigwedge_{x \in N} x \leqslant t$ holds.

We denote the set of upper bounds of N by $\mathsf{Ma}\, N$ (majorant of N) and write the definition as follows:

(1) $$t \in \mathsf{Ma}\, N \leftrightharpoons \bigwedge_{x \in N} x \leqslant t.$$

Correspondingly we denote the set of *lower bounds* $\mathsf{Mi}\, N$ (minorant of N) by

(2) $$v \in \mathsf{Mi}\, N \leftrightharpoons \bigwedge_{x \in N} v \leqslant x.$$

Thus it is easy to see that:

(3) From $N_1 \subseteq N_2$ it follows that $\mathsf{Ma}\, N_2 \subseteq \mathsf{Ma}\, N_1$ and $\mathsf{Mi}\, N_2 \subseteq \mathsf{Mi}\, N_1$;

(4.1) $$\mathsf{Mi}(\mathsf{Ma}\, N) \supseteq N,$$

(4.2) $$\mathsf{Ma}(\mathsf{Mi}\, N) \supseteq N.$$

The schematic Fig. 5 serves as an illustration.

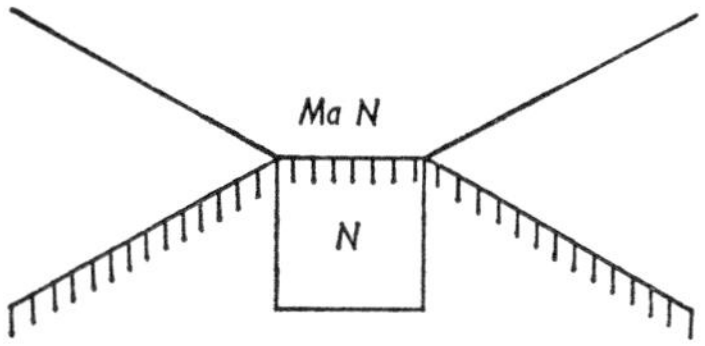

Fig. 5. Shaded: $\mathsf{Mi}(\mathsf{Ma}\, N)$.

From (3) and (4.1) it follows that

$$\mathsf{Ma}(\mathsf{Mi}(\mathsf{Ma}\,N)) \subseteq \mathsf{Ma}\,N;$$

from (4.2) with Ma N in place of N it follows that:

$$\mathsf{Ma}(\mathsf{Mi}(\mathsf{Ma}\,N)) \supseteq \mathsf{Ma}\,N.$$

So we obtain

(5) $\mathsf{Ma}(\mathsf{Mi}(\mathsf{Ma}\,N)) = \mathsf{Ma}\,N$ and similarly $\mathsf{Mi}(\mathsf{Ma}(\mathsf{Mi}\,N)) = \mathsf{Mi}\,N$.

An element s is called an *upper limit* of N if

(6.1) s is an upper bound of N, i.e. if

$$s \in \mathsf{Ma}\,N, \text{ in other words } \bigwedge_{x \in N} x \leqslant s$$

(6.2) *and* if s is smaller than or equal to every other upper bound of N, i.e. if

$$t \in \mathsf{Ma}\,N \rightarrow s \leqslant r, \text{ i.e. } s \in \mathsf{Mi}(\mathsf{Ma}\,N)$$

$$\text{or } \bigwedge_{t} (\bigwedge_{x \in N} x \leqslant t \rightarrow s \leqslant t).$$

We denote the set of upper limits of N by *sup* N and combine (6.1) and (6.2) to give

(7) $$s \in sup\ N \leftrightharpoons s \in \mathsf{Ma}\,N \cap \mathsf{Mi}(\mathsf{Ma}\,N).$$

Correspondingly *inf* N is defined as the set of lower limits of N:

(8) $$u \in inf\ N \leftrightharpoons u \in \mathsf{Mi}\,N \cap \mathsf{Ma}(\mathsf{Mi}\,N),$$

i.e. $$\bigwedge_{x \in N} u \leqslant x \wedge \bigwedge_{w} (\bigwedge_{x \in N} w \leqslant x \rightarrow w \leqslant u).$$

(6.2) implies that if s_1, s_2 are two upper limits of N, then $s_1 \leqslant s_2$ and $s_2 \leqslant s_1$. If $\leqslant$ is anti-symmetric, i.e. if $(M, \leqslant)$ is an ordered set, then N can have at most one upper limit and similarly at most one lower limit. In that case we denote the upper limit[1] by

$$s = sup\ N = \bigsqcup_{x \in N} x = \bigsqcup_{N} x$$

[1] This means that we use *sup* N (and also *inf* N) both for a subset of M and, in case this subset consists of a single element, for this element itself. The symbols $\bigsqcup$, $\sqcup$, $\bigsqcap$, $\sqcap$ are used only for elements (and only in ordered sets); we read them as 'union' and 'intersection'.

and if N consists of two elements a, b only, we write $s = a \sqcup b$. We write down the definition once more, because it is used frequently:

(9) $$a \leqslant a \sqcup b \wedge b \leqslant a \sqcup b \wedge \bigwedge_t (a \leqslant t \wedge b \leqslant t \rightarrow a \sqcup b \leqslant t).$$

This corresponds to the rules (Br3) and (Br6) of Introduction § 3, by which the adjunction of propositions was characterized.

Similarly we write in an ordered set $(M, \leqslant)$

$$u = inf\, N = \prod_{x \in N} x = \prod_N x.$$

The definition for $u = inf\{a, b\} = a \sqcap b$ is

(10) $$a \sqcap b \leqslant a \wedge a \sqcap b \leqslant b \wedge \bigwedge_w (w \leqslant a \wedge w \leqslant b \rightarrow w \leqslant a \sqcap b).$$

It corresponds to the rules (Br2) and (Br5) of Introduction § 3, by which the conjunction of propositions was characterized.

2.2. *Existence*

It is well known that even in a linearly ordered set every subset need not have an upper limit. For example, in the set of rational numbers ordered by $\underset{z}{\leqslant}$ the subset of numbers x with $x^2 \underset{z}{\leqslant} 2$ has no upper limit. In the set $M = \{a, b, c\}$ with the order relation given by Fig. 6 (page 41) the set M itself has no lower bound.

Under assumptions that are often satisfied in algebra we can deduce the existence of upper limits from that of lower limits. We shall have to quote this theorem several times and for this purpose we call it the *theorem of the upper limit*:

Theorem. Suppose that $(M, \leqslant)$ is a quasi-ordered set; (I) that for every non-empty subset of M there exists at least one lower limit in M; (II) that for the set $N \subseteq M$ there exists (at least) one upper bound in M; then there exists (at least one and if $(M, \leqslant)$ is ordered, precisely) one upper limit of N, and in fact

$$sup\, N = inf(\mathsf{Ma}\, N).$$

Proof. By hypothesis (II), Ma N is not empty. Hence by hypothesis (I) $inf(\mathsf{Ma}\, N)$ is not empty.

By definition (8) we have $inf(\mathsf{Ma}\, N) = \mathsf{Mi}(\mathsf{Ma}\, N) \cap \mathsf{Ma}(\mathsf{Mi}(\mathsf{Ma}\, N))$ and by (5) $= \mathsf{Mi}(\mathsf{Ma}\, N) \cap \mathsf{Ma}\, N$. But this is the definition of *sup* N.

Hypothesis (II) is always satisfied when M consists of subsets of a set e, e itself belongs to M, and the order relation is inclusion $\subseteq$.

For example, if M consists of the subgroups of a group e, then in addition the intersection of an arbitrary number of subgroups is again a subgroup. From this it follows that for every subset N of M a lower limit exists, namely $\underset{N}{\sqcap}\, x = \underset{N}{\cap}\, x$. Since every subgroup contains the unit element of the group, $\underset{N}{\cap}\, x$ is not empty. Thus hypothesis (I) is satisfied. The same holds, for example, for rings and fields, and more generally for every 'intersection hereditary structure'. This concept will be explained more accurately in Chapter IV.

According to the existence of upper and lower limits, one distinguishes classes of quasi-ordered sets:

A *quasi-ordered set* $(M, \leqslant)$ is called *directed* if M contains an upper bound of any two of its elements (we also say: a common upper element). (One could call this 'directed above' and define the dual concept 'directed below' correspondingly; however, we shall not need this.)

An *ordered set* $(M, \leqslant)$ is called $\sqcup$-*semi-lattice* (supremum semi-lattice) if M contains an upper limit of any two elements; $(M, \leqslant)$ is called *complete* $\sqcup$-*lattice* if M contains an upper limit of every subset. Correspondingly one defines $\sqcap$-semi-lattice and complete $\sqcap$-semi-lattice. If $(M, \leqslant)$ is simultaneously a $\sqcup$- and a $\sqcap$-semi-lattice, then $(M, \leqslant)$ is called a *lattice*. A *complete lattice* is defined correspondingly. If the existence of the upper and lower limit is assumed for countable sets only, then one talks of σ-completeness and a σ-lattice, respectively.

A particular case of the theorem of the upper limit is the following: if $(M, \leqslant)$ is a complete $\sqcap$-semi-lattice and if there is an upper bound for M itself (which of course then belongs to M and is therefore an upper limit), then $(M, \leqslant)$ is a complete lattice.

§ 3. Maximal and minimal elements

In this section, let $(M, \leqslant)$ always be an ordered set. For sets that are only quasi-ordered the definitions lose their meaning, although no explicit use is made of anti-symmetry.

Definition. Let $N \subseteq M$; m is called a *maximal element* of N if $m \in N$ and N contains no larger element, i.e. if

$$m \in N \text{ and } \bigwedge_{x \in N} (m \leqslant x \rightarrow m = x).$$

A maximal element need not be an upper limit; for example N may contain several maximal elements, but at most one upper limit. In Fig. 6 let $M=\{a,b,c\}$, $N=\{a,b\}$. N has the maximal elements a and b and the upper limit c.

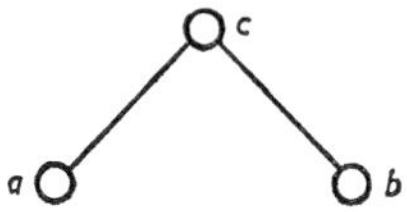

Fig. 6

However, if there is an upper limit s for N and s is itself an element of N, then s is a maximal element of N and N contains no further maximal element. The proof follows immediately from the relevant definitions.

In this case s has the property

$$s \in N \wedge \bigwedge_{x \in N} x \leqslant s.$$

An element with this property is called the *greatest element of N* (in lattices: the *unit element*). This concept is to be distinguished carefully both from that of the upper limit and that of the maximal element.

If N is *directed*, i.e. for any two elements contains a common upper element, then N can contain at most one maximal element, and this is then the greatest element.

> *Proof.* Let m be a maximal, x an arbitrary, element of N. Then there exists $r \in N$, such that $m \leqslant r \wedge x \leqslant r$. Since m is maximal, it follows that $m=r$, hence $\bigwedge_{x \in N} x \leqslant m$.

Similarly one defines:
p is called a *minimal element* of N if

$$p \in N \text{ and } \bigwedge_{x \in N} (x \leqslant p \rightarrow x = p);$$

n is called the *smallest element* (in lattices: the *null element*) of N if

$$n \in N \text{ and } \bigwedge_{x \in N} n \leqslant x.$$

The upper neighbours of the null element are called *atoms*, or in geometrical applications *points*.

§ 4. Criteria for the existence of maximal or minimal elements

4.1. Finite length

Definition. If in an ordered set $(M, \leqslant)$ every *descending sequence* $a_0 \geqslant a_1 \geqslant a_2 \geqslant \ldots$ contains at most a finite number of distinct elements, then $(M, \leqslant)$ is said to be *of finite length downwards* (one also says: $(M, \leqslant)$ satisfies the descending chain condition). If every *ascending sequence* $a_0 \leqslant a_1 \leqslant a_2 \leqslant \ldots$ contains at most a finite number of distinct elements, then $(M, \leqslant)$ is said to be *of finite length upwards.* If both conditions hold, then $(M, \leqslant)$ is said to be *of finite length.*

The term *finite length* is sometimes defined differently, namely by the fact that every chain *between two fixed elements* has finite length; in this case we say: *of bounded finite length.*

By definition a descending or ascending sequence is linearly ordered, i.e. a chain (see Chapter II, § 1.1). For a finite chain $a_0 \leqslant a_1 \leqslant \ldots \leqslant a_l$, l is called the *length* of the chain. However, it makes sense to apply this concept only to *proper* chains, i.e. such chains whose terms are distinct from one another.

Theorem. If $(M, \leqslant)$ is of finite length upwards, then M has at least a maximal element; in fact, for every $a \in M$ there exists a maximal element m with $a \leqslant m$.

Proof. If a is not itself a maximal element, then by definition of the maximal element in M there exists an $a_1 > a$. A repetition of this argument leads to an ascending chain which by assumption breaks off after a finite number of terms. Its last element is maximal and $\geqslant a$.

If in addition $(M, \leqslant)$ is directed, then (by § 3) a maximal element is a greatest element. A special case of this is the theorem: if a $\sqcup$-semi-lattice is of finite length upwards, then it contains a unit element.

Of course, the corresponding theorems hold for ordered sets of finite length downwards.

4.2. The maximal principle

A criterion for the existence of maximal elements in an ordered set is given by the maximal principle, which goes back to Kuratowski, Hausdorff, and Zorn and is often called *Zorn's Lemma*, because he gave a formulation of it which is particularly suitable for algebra and which has important applications. There are several equivalent statements; let us consider the following:

> If in an ordered set $(M, \leqslant)$ there is an upper bound for every linearly ordered subset (relative to the order of M), then M contains a maximal element.

We shall prove this theorem for the case when $M = \{a_1, a_2, \ldots\}$ is countable, in the (inessentially) stronger form that for every element a_k of M there is a maximal element $a_m \geqslant a_k$.

Either a_k is itself a maximal element, or there is a smallest natural number k_1 with $a_{k_1} > a_k$. Either a_{k_1} is a maximal element, or there is a smallest k_2 with $a_{k_2} > a_{k_1}$, and here $k_2 > k_1$, etc.

Either the construction ends after a finite number of steps with a maximal element a_{k_m}, or there exists an infinite sequence of natural numbers k_i with $k_{i+1} > k_i$ and $a_{k_{i+1}} > a_{k_i}$. We claim that the second case leads to a contradiction. The linearly ordered set $\{a_{k_i}\}$ would have, by hypothesis, an upper bound a_m, so that

$$(*) \qquad a_{k_i} \leqslant a_m \text{ for all } k_i.$$

On the other hand, in the infinite sequence of natural numbers k_i there would be two numbers k_i, k_{i+1} such that $k_i \leqslant m \leqslant k_{i+1}$. But since $a_m \geqslant a_{k_i}$ and k_{i+1} is the smallest number $> k_i$ with $a_{k_{i+1}} > a_{k_i}$, it follows that $a_m = a_{k_i}$ or $m = k_{i+1}$. In either case we would have $a_m < a_{k_{i+2}}$, in contradiction to (*).

For uncountable sets, instead of countability one has to use well-ordering. Such proofs can be found in many books.[1] Some fundamental doubts have been pointed out by Lorenzen.[2]

In applications the elements of M are often subsets of a set (for example, ideals of a lattice, as in Chapter VII, § 2.5); if one can then show that for every linearly ordered set L (of ideals) the union $v = \bigcup_L a_i$ is an element of M (which in our example is again an ideal), then v is an upper bound of L.

[1] A. A. Fraenkel, 'Abstract Set Theory', rev. ed. Amsterdam 1961. B. Rotman and G. T. Kneebone, 'The Theory of Sets and Transfinite Numbers', London 1966. P. Suppes, 'Axiomatic Set Theory', Princeton 1960.

[2] P. Lorenzen, 'Über den Kettensatz der Mengenlehre', *Archiv d. Math.*, **9**, 1958, 1–6.

CHAPTER III

Directed Sets and Lattices

An ordered set $(M, \leqslant)$ may split into subsets in such a way that there is no order relation between two elements from distinct subsets. (See Fig. 4b.) This will now be excluded by additional postulates, such as:

1) M contains a common upper element (an upper bound) of any two elements, hence M is *directed*;

2) M contains a least common upper element (an upper limit) $a \sqcup b$ of any two elements a, b, hence M is a $\sqcup$-semi-lattice;

1a) 2a) similarly with lower bound, lower limit ($a \sqcap b$), $\sqcap$-semi-lattice;

3) M contains with any two elements a and b, also $a \sqcup b$ and $a \sqcap b$, and hence is a *lattice*.

Directed sets play an important role in the theory of convergence. The postulate of anti-symmetry can be omitted here; this application will be treated in § 1. The rest of the chapter deals with lattices, specifically with those properties by which lattices are generally characterized.

§ 1. Directed sets in the theory of convergence

Let $\{a_n\}$, $\{b_n\}$ be convergent sequences of real numbers and $\lim_{n\to\infty} a_n = a$, $\lim_{n\to\infty} b_n = b$. Let $c_n = a_n + b_n$. Then we have, of course, $\lim_{n\to\infty} c_n = a+b$. We assume the proof as known and only wish to indicate a particular point in it. One has to show:

$$(1) \qquad \bigwedge_{\epsilon>0} \bigvee_{n_0} \bigwedge_{n} n > n_0 \rightarrow |a_n + b_n - (a+b)| < \epsilon.$$

In words: for every $\epsilon > 0$ a natural number n_0 can be found such that for every n that is greater than n_0, $|a_n+b_n-(a+b)| < \epsilon$.

By assumption there is an n_1 and n_2 such that

$$n > n_1 \rightarrow |a_n - a| < \epsilon/2,$$

$$n > n_2 \rightarrow |b_n - b| < \epsilon/2.$$

If one then chooses for n_0 the larger of the two numbers n_1 and n_2 (or if $n_1 = n_2$, then $n_0 = n_1 = n_2$), (1) is satisfied. This is the usual argument. But all that is needed is that there exists an n_0 with $n_0 \geqslant n_1$ and $n_0 \geqslant n_2$; i.e. one only needs the index set—here the set of natural numbers—to be a set quasi-ordered by $\leqslant$ in which there exists a common upper element for any two elements, i.e. to be a directed set.

Also it does not matter that on the right-hand side of $\rightarrow$ we have the absolute value of the difference of two real numbers. It suffices if in place of $|x-y|$ a 'distance function' $\delta(x,y)$ is used, which satisfies by definition the following axioms:

$$\delta(x,y) \quad \text{is a real number} \geqslant 0,$$

$$\delta(x,y) \quad = 0 \leftrightarrow x = y,$$

$$\delta(x,y) \quad = \delta(y,x),$$

$$\delta(x,y) + \delta(y,z) \geqslant \delta(x,z) \text{ (triangle inequality).}$$

If a distance function δ is defined in a set M, then (M, δ) is called a *metric space*. It is in fact sufficient for M to carry a topological structure; however, here we do not want to go that far. In place of $\delta(x,y)$ we shall write again $|x-y|$.

We can now introduce a general notion of convergent sequences: let $(N, \leqslant)$ be a directed set, A a mapping of N into a metric space (M, δ). The image of n under the mapping A is denoted by a_n or $a(n)$. A is called a Moore-Smith sequence. One defines: the Moore-Smith sequence A *converges* to $a \in M$ if

$$\bigwedge_{\epsilon>0} \bigvee_{n_0 \in N} \bigwedge_{n \in N} n \geqslant n_0 \rightarrow \delta(a_n, a) \underset{z}{\leqslant} \epsilon.$$

(For a general topological space the definition would be: for every neighbourhood $U(a)$ there is an n_0 in N such that for every $n \geqslant n_0$ we have $a_n \in U(a)$.)

This definition comprises not only the convergence of a numerical sequence, but also the convergence of a complex function $f(z)$ at a point z_0. Here the 'index set' is the set of complex numbers and for the quasi-order one takes the distance from z_0,

$$z_1 \geqslant z_2 \leftrightarrows |z_1 - z_0| \underset{z}{\leqslant} |z_2 - z_0|,$$

for the mapping one takes the function f, for the distance function $\delta(w_1, w_2) = |w_2 - w_1|$. Then the general definition gives: $f(z)$ converges, as z goes to z_0, to the value w_0 if

$$\bigwedge_{\epsilon>0} \bigvee_{z_1} \bigwedge_{z} z \geqslant z_1 \rightarrow |f(z) - w_0| \underset{z}{\leqslant} \epsilon.$$

The general definition of convergence also comprises the definition of the Riemann integral.

In order to define $\int_a^b f(x)\mathrm{d}x$ one divides the closed interval (a, b) into finitely many sub-intervals. With every such division $\mathfrak{Z}$ an upper sum $O(\mathfrak{Z})$ and a lower sum $U(\mathfrak{Z})$ is associated. Let their difference be $D(\mathfrak{Z})$.

Now we introduce in the set Z of divisions the following order relation: $\mathfrak{Z}_1$ is said to be finer (or coarser) than $\mathfrak{Z}_2$, written $\mathfrak{Z}_1 \geqslant \mathfrak{Z}_2$, if every division point belonging to $\mathfrak{Z}_2$ also belongs to $\mathfrak{Z}_1$. If one understands by $\mathfrak{Z}_i$ the set of division points, then $\mathfrak{Z}_1 \geqslant \mathfrak{Z}_2$ if $\mathfrak{Z}_2 \subseteq \mathfrak{Z}_1$. It is easy to verify that this is an order relation. The set of divisions is directed under this relation, because any two divisions always have a common refinement.

The Riemann integral exists, by definition, precisely if

$$lim\ D(\mathfrak{Z}) = 0$$

where *lim* is to be taken in the sense of the above definition.

In this way the definitions of convergence of a sequence, convergence of a function, and the existence of the Riemann integral are combined under a uniform scheme. Of course, the point is to find out whether the general assumptions made here are still sufficient to prove the theorems that are required in a convergence theory. It is not the object of the present book to carry through this programme.

§ 2. Lattices. Examples

In what follows we shall deal only with lattices, that is ordered sets $(V, \leqslant)$ in which for any two elements a and b of V there exist one (and on account of (as) only one) least common upper element (supremum) $a \sqcup b$ and precisely one greatest common lower element (infimum) $a \sqcap b$.

2.1. Some finite lattices

Figure 7 shows the order diagram of all lattices that consist of 2, 3, 4, or 5 elements. (The reader should check that there are no others.)

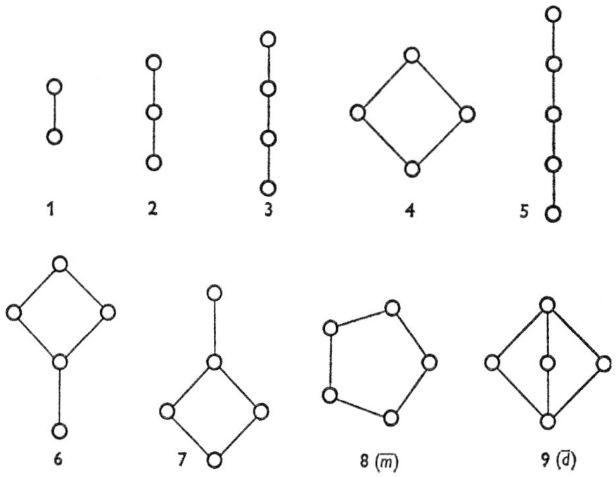

Fig. 7

2.2. Linearly ordered sets and direct products

Examples 1, 2, 3, 5 represent linearly ordered sets. Quite generally: every linearly ordered set is a lattice. Indeed, for any two elements we have $a \leqslant b$ or $b \leqslant a$. In the former case we have $a \sqcap b = a$ and $a \sqcup b = b$, in the latter case $a \sqcap b = b$, $a \sqcup b = a$.

We obtain further examples by the formation of the *direct product.*

Let $(V_1, \leqslant_1)$, $(V_2, \leqslant_2)$ be two lattices. We form the cartesian product $V = V_1 \times V_2$, that is, the set of all pairs $x = (x_1, x_2)$, $x_1 \in V_1$, $x_2 \in V_2$, and define:

$$(x_1, x_2) \leqslant (y_1, y_2) \ \Leftrightarrow \ x_1 \leqslant_1 y_1 \wedge x_2 \leqslant_2 y_2.$$

$(V, \leqslant)$ is called the direct product of $(V_1, \leqslant_1)$ and $(V_2, \leqslant_2)$, written $(V_1, \leqslant_1) \times (V_2, \leqslant_2)$. The subscripts on the order symbols may be omitted because it is clear from the elements between which the symbol stands which of the three relations is meant.

It is easily seen that $\leqslant$ in V is an order relation, i.e. reflexive, transitive, and anti-symmetric. The fact that $(V, \leqslant)$ is a lattice can be seen as follows: for (x_1,x_2), (y_1,y_2) we form

$$d = (x_1 \sqcap y_1, x_2 \sqcap y_2).$$

1) From $x_i \sqcap y_i \leqslant x_i$ and $x_i \sqcap y_i \leqslant y_i$ it follows that $d \leqslant (x_1,x_2)$ and $d \leqslant (y_1,y_2)$.

2) Suppose that $(c_1,c_2) \leqslant (x_1,x_2)$ and $(c_1,c_2) \leqslant (y_1,y_2)$.
Then by definition

$$c_1 \leqslant x_1 \text{ and } c_1 \leqslant y_1, \text{ hence } c_1 \leqslant x_1 \sqcap y_1,$$
$$c_2 \leqslant x_2 \text{ and } c_2 \leqslant y_2, \text{ hence } c_2 \leqslant x_2 \sqcap y_2,$$

hence $(c_1,c_2) \leqslant d$.
Thus we have shown: $(x_1 \sqcap y_1, x_2 \sqcap y_2) = (x_1, x_2) \sqcap (y_1,y_2)$.
Similarly we see: $(x_1 \sqcup y_1, x_2 \sqcup y_2) = (x_1, x_2) \sqcup (y_1, y_2)$.

Thus we have proved that the direct product of two lattices is a lattice.

By the same method of proof it can be shown that the direct product of two complete lattices is a complete lattice.

We can form the direct product for an arbitrary number of factors. Let us consider the direct product of a countable number of lattices $(V_i, \leqslant_i)$, $i=1,2,\ldots$ We form the set $\mathfrak{V}$ of sequences $\mathfrak{a}=(\alpha_1,\alpha_2\ldots)$, $\alpha_i \in V_i$, and define: $\mathfrak{a} \leqslant \mathfrak{b} \leftrightharpoons \bigwedge\limits_i \alpha_i \leqslant_i \beta_i$. It can be shown that this is an order relation and that $(\mathfrak{V}, \leqslant)$ is a lattice.

A special case: for every natural number i let $(V_i, \leqslant_i) = (N, \underset{z}{\leqslant})$ be the lattice of natural numbers with $\underset{z}{\leqslant}$ as order. The set $\mathfrak{V}_E$ of finite sequences forms a sub-lattice $(\mathfrak{V}_E, \leqslant) \subseteq (\mathfrak{V}, \leqslant)$, as is easy to prove.

Now we can indicate a one-to-one and 'order preserving' mapping of the ordered set $(N, |)$, i.e. the set of natural numbers with divisibility as order, onto $(\mathfrak{V}_E, \leqslant)$ in the following way: let p_1, p_2,... be the prime numbers ordered by increasing magnitude. Then every natural number has a unique decomposition into prime factors,

$$a = p_1^{a_1} \cdot p_2^{a_2} \ldots p_n^{a_n},$$

i.e. with every natural number a we can associate bi-uniquely a finite sequence $\mathfrak{a} = (\alpha_1, \alpha_2, \ldots, \alpha_n)$ of natural numbers. $a|b$ holds if and only if $\bigwedge\limits_i \alpha_i \underset{z}{\leqslant} \beta_i$, i.e. $\mathfrak{a} \leqslant \mathfrak{b}$. From this it follows that $(N, |)$ is a lattice. For, any two elements a and b of N correspond to two elements $\mathfrak{a}$ and $\mathfrak{b}$ of $\mathfrak{B}_E$. $\mathfrak{d} = \mathfrak{a} \sqcap \mathfrak{b}$ is the element of $\mathfrak{B}_E$ uniquely determined by

$$\mathfrak{d} \leqslant \mathfrak{a} \wedge \mathfrak{d} \leqslant \mathfrak{b} \text{ and } \bigwedge_{\mathfrak{c}} \mathfrak{c} \leqslant \mathfrak{a} \wedge \mathfrak{c} \leqslant \mathfrak{b} \rightarrow \mathfrak{c} \leqslant \mathfrak{d}.$$

The element $d \in N$ associated with $\mathfrak{d}$ then has the same properties relative to a and b. So the existence of $a \sqcap b$ is established. The existence of $a \sqcup b$ can be similarly shown.

Even the divisors of, say, 3 form a lattice; its order diagram is Fig. 7, no. 1; no. 2 can be regarded as the order diagram of the divisors of 4. As their direct product one obtains the lattice of the divisors of 12 whose order diagram is represented in Fig. 8.

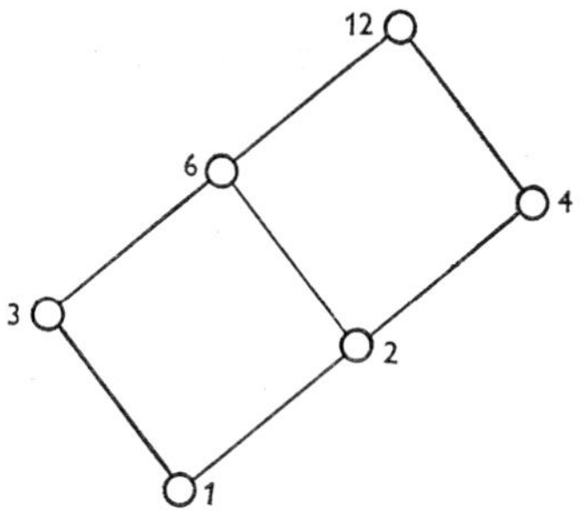

Fig. 8

In these lattices the least common upper element is the least common multiple, the greatest common lower element is the greatest common divisor.

2.3. Subsets of a set

$(\mathfrak{P}e, \subseteq)$, i.e. the set $\mathfrak{P}e$ of all subsets of a set e with inclusion as the order relation, forms a (complete) lattice.

$a \sqcup b$ is by definition the least set containing a and b. On the other hand, the union $a \cup b$ is defined by

(2) $$\xi \in a \cup b \leftrightharpoons \xi \in a \vee \xi \in b,$$

i.e. it consists of precisely those elements that belong to a or to b (or to both). Instead of (2) we also write

(3) $$a \cup b = \{\xi, \xi \in a \vee \xi \in b\}.$$

Let us show that $a \sqcup b = a \cup b$. For this purpose we apply the rules (Br) (Introduction, § 3) to the propositions

$$A \leftrightharpoons \xi \in a, B \leftrightharpoons \xi \in b, C \leftrightharpoons \xi \in c.$$

$A \Rightarrow A \vee B$ then becomes $\xi \in a \to \xi \in a \vee \xi \in b$, i.e. $\xi \in a \cup b$. But this means (by Chapter I, § 1)

(4.1) $$a \subseteq a \cup b,$$

(4.2) $$b \subseteq a \cup b.$$

On the other hand, if c is a set with $a \subseteq c$ and $b \subseteq c$, we have

$$\xi \in a \to \xi \in c, \xi \in b \to \xi \in c.$$

Then it follows by (Br6) that

$$\xi \in a \vee \xi \in b \to \xi \in c,$$

i.e. by (3), $\xi \in a \cup b \to \xi \in c$

and this means: $$a \cup b \subseteq c.$$

Hence we have

(5) $$a \subseteq c \wedge b \subseteq c \to a \cup b \subseteq c.$$

But (4.1) (4.2) and (5) constitute precisely the definition of $a \sqcup b$. We have given this proof in so much detail because we wanted to illustrate the connections between the symbols $\sqcup, \cup, \vee$. The connections between $\sqcap, \cap, \wedge$ are similar; we have also

$$a \sqcap b = a \cap b.$$

With the help of the rule for quantifiers (page 22) one proves similarly that for the lattice $(\mathfrak{P}e, \subseteq)$

$$\bigcup_N x = \bigsqcup_N x \text{ and } \bigcap_N x = \mathop{\sqcap}_N x.$$

(For the definition see Chapter I, § 1, and Chapter II, § 2.1.)

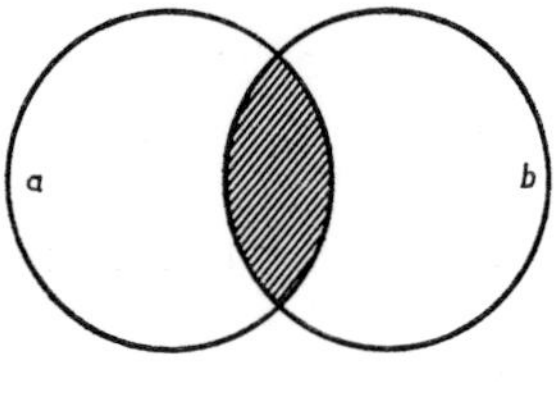

Fig. 9a

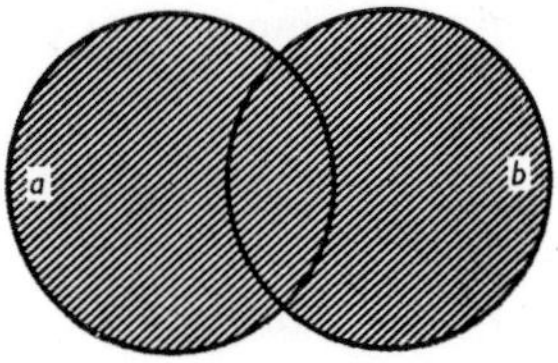

Fig. 9b

Many properties of lattices can be simply illustrated by choosing e, for example, as the set of points of a plane or of a rectangle in the plane. In Fig. 9a the shaded area is $a \cap b$, in Fig. 9b $a \cup b$. Fig. 10 shows the order diagram for $(\mathfrak{P}e, \subseteq)$, if e consists of the four elements $\alpha, \beta, \gamma, \epsilon$. The emphasized part of the figure refers to the first example of the next section.

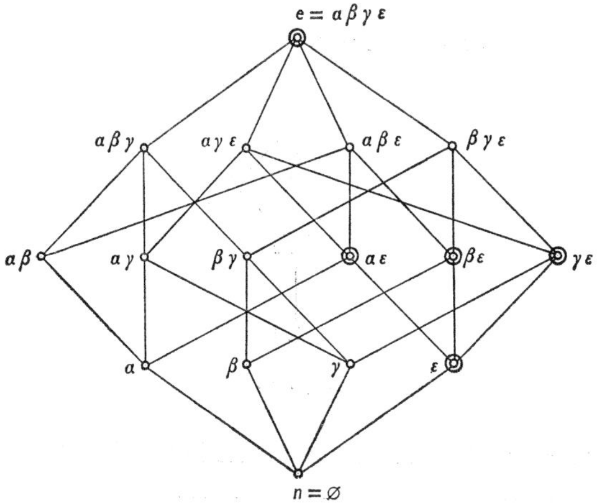

Fig. 10

2.4. Subgroups of a group

If we consider a subset $G \subseteq \mathfrak{P}e$, then $(G, \subseteq)$ is again an ordered set, but it need not be a lattice; and even if $(G, \subseteq)$ is a lattice, we need not have $a \sqcap b = a \cap b$ and $a \sqcup b = a \cup b$, namely if $a \cap b$ or $a \cup b$ are not contained in G.

The proof of the preceding section shows that if $a \cup b \in G$, then $a \cup b = a \sqcup b$, and if $a \cap b \in G$, then $a \cap b = a \sqcap b$.

Suppose, for example, that in e an operation '.' is defined such that $(e, .)$ is a group. Let G be the set of subgroups of e. For any a and b if $a \in G$ and $b \in G$ then $a \cap b \in G$, hence $a \sqcap b = a \cap b$. However, the set-theoretical union of two subgroups is not always a subgroup.

Example 1. If $\alpha, \beta, \gamma, \epsilon$ are the elements of the Klein Four group, with ϵ the unit element, $\alpha^2 = \beta^2 = \gamma^2 = \epsilon$, $\alpha\beta = \gamma$, then only the subsets $\{\epsilon\}, \{\epsilon, \alpha\}, \{\epsilon, \beta\}, \{\epsilon, \gamma\}, \{\epsilon, \alpha, \beta, \gamma\}$ are subgroups. They are distinguished in Fig. 10.

Example 2. The group e of quaternion units ± 1, $\pm i$, $\pm j$, $\pm k$ with $i^2=j^2=k^2=-1$, $ij=k=-ji$, $jk=i=-kj$, $ki=j=-ik$ has as its subgroups

$$n = \{1\},$$

$$a = \{+1, -1\},$$

$$b_i = \{\pm 1, \pm i\}, b_j = \{\pm 1, \pm j\}, b_k = \{\pm 1, \pm k\}.$$

The order diagram is shown in Fig. 11.

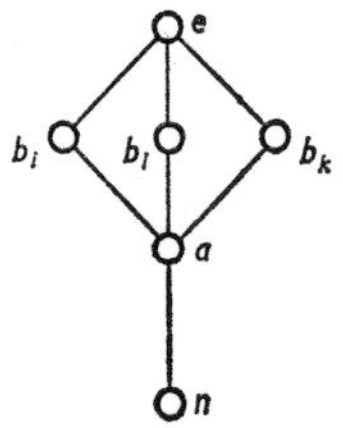

Fig. 11

This is an example of an atomic lattice in which not every element can be represented as a union of atoms. (See Chapter VII, § 1.4.)

Example 3. Let G be the direct product of three cyclic groups of order 2, in other words the commutative group generated by the elements ϵ (unit element), α, β, γ with $\alpha^2=\beta^2=\gamma^2=\epsilon$. Its elements are

$$\epsilon, \alpha, \beta, \gamma, \alpha\beta, \beta\gamma, \gamma\alpha, \alpha\beta\gamma;$$

its subgroups are

$$n = \{\epsilon\},$$

$$p_1 = \{\epsilon, \alpha\}, \qquad g_1 = \{\epsilon, \alpha, \beta, \alpha\beta\},$$

$$p_2 = \{\epsilon, \beta\}, \qquad g_2 = \{\epsilon, \alpha, \gamma, \alpha\gamma\},$$

$$p_3 = \{\epsilon, \gamma\}, \qquad g_3 = \{\epsilon, \beta, \gamma, \beta\gamma\},$$

$$p_4 = \{\epsilon, \alpha\beta\}, \qquad g_4 = \{\epsilon, \alpha, \beta\gamma, \alpha\beta\gamma\},$$

$$p_5 = \{\epsilon, \beta\gamma\}, \qquad g_5 = \{\epsilon, \beta, \gamma\alpha, \alpha\beta\gamma\},$$

$$p_6 = \{\epsilon, \gamma\alpha\}, \qquad g_6 = \{\epsilon, \gamma, \alpha\beta, \alpha\beta\gamma\},$$

$$p_7 = \{\epsilon, \alpha\beta\gamma\}, \qquad g_7 = \{\epsilon, \alpha\beta, \beta\gamma, \gamma\alpha\}.$$

The drawing of the order diagram is left to the reader. Let us give a geometric interpretation of this lattice. For this purpose we write the elements in the form

$$\xi = \alpha^{\xi_1}.\beta^{\xi_2}.\gamma^{\xi_3}.$$

So we can represent every element by the triplet $(\xi_1, \xi_2, \xi_3) = \mathfrak{x}$, where ξ_i can assume the values 0 and 1. To the product ξ_η there corresponds the triplet $(\xi_i + \eta_i)$, $i = 1, 2, 3$, where one has to calculate modulo 2, i.e. to set $1+1=0$. Excluding the triplet $(0,0,0) = \epsilon$ we interpret the subgroups $p_1, \ldots, p_7$ as points as in Fig. 12. Then the subgroups $g_1, \ldots g_7$ are precisely the lines of Fig. 12 including the circle (g_7) which we shall also call a line. The equations of these lines, as one can verify from the figure, are

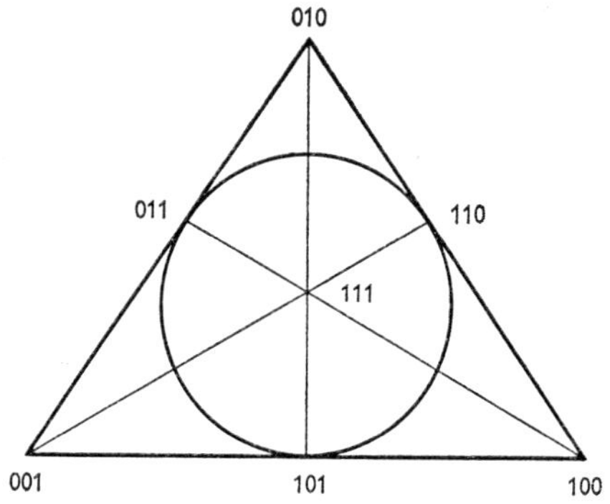

Fig. 12

$$\xi_1 = 0,\ \xi_2 = 0,\ \xi_3 = 0,$$
$$\xi_1 + \xi_2 = 0 \text{ (or, which is the same modulo 2: } \xi_1 = \xi_2),$$
$$\xi_2 + \xi_3 = 0,$$
$$\xi_3 + \xi_1 = 0,$$
$$\xi_1 + \xi_2 + \xi_3 = 0,$$

i.e. they are all the equations of the form

$$\eta_1 \xi_1 + \eta_2 \xi_2 + \eta_3 \xi_3 = 0,$$

where (ξ_1, ξ_2, ξ_3) ranges over all 0-1 triplets except $(0,0,0)$. This can be expressed as follows: we have the projective plane over the prime field of characteristic 2.

Quite generally, projective geometry can be interpreted in terms of lattice theory. Let us discuss the three-dimensional projective space P_3 over the field of real numbers which we assume here as (intuitively) known (see Chapter V, § 6). Let the elements of V be the empty set $\varnothing$, the points, lines, and planes of P_3, and P_3 itself. We call them linear subspaces of P_3. Let the order relation be containedness $\subseteq$. Since we are dealing with subsets of a set (the set of points of P_3), this is in fact an order relation. Union (supremum) of two subspaces is the least subspace containing both, hence in general not the set-theoretical union; infimum is the (set-theoretical) intersection.

We have here a particular case of a subgroup lattice, because P_3 can be regarded as a vector space of dimension 4 over the field of real numbers, and a vector space is a commutative group (under addition) with operators (the operator domain is the field of real numbers). (See Chapter V, § 4.)

§ 3. Algebraic characterization of lattices

The operations $\sqcap$ and $\sqcup$ satisfy:

the commutative laws

(C1) $a \sqcap b = b \sqcap a,$ (C2) $a \sqcup b = b \sqcup a,$

the associative laws

(A1) $a \sqcap (b \sqcap c) = (a \sqcap b) \sqcap c,$ (A2) $a \sqcup (b \sqcup c) = (a \sqcup b) \sqcup c,$

the absorption laws

(Ab1) $a \sqcap (a \sqcup b) = a,$ (Ab2) $a \sqcup (a \sqcap b) = a.$

The reader should illustrate the absorption laws by a part of an order diagram or by the example of point sets in a plane (Fig. 13).

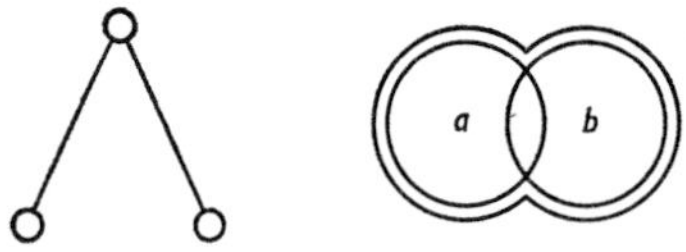

Fig. 13

$a \sqcap (a \sqcup b) = a$ b $a \sqcup b$ surrounded twice

Proof. (C1). Let $a \sqcap b = c$, $b \sqcap a = d$.
Then by definition of $\sqcap$: $c \leqslant a \wedge c \leqslant b$.

Since the connection of propositions by $\wedge$ is commutative:

$$c \leqslant b \wedge c \leqslant a,$$

hence again by definition of $\sqcap$: $c \leqslant b \sqcap a = d$. Similarly we can prove that $d \leqslant c$.

(A1). Let $a \sqcap (b \sqcap c) = p$, $(a \sqcap b) \sqcap c = q$.

Then $$p \leqslant a \wedge p \leqslant b \sqcap c,$$

hence $$p \leqslant a \wedge (p \leqslant b \wedge p \leqslant c).$$

Since the connection of propositions by $\wedge$ is associative, this implies

$$(p \leqslant a \wedge p \leqslant b) \wedge p \leqslant c,$$

i.e. $$p \leqslant a \sqcap b \wedge p \leqslant c,$$

i.e. $$p \leqslant (a \sqcap b) \sqcap c = q.$$

Similarly one proves that $q \leqslant p$.

So the proofs are based on the validity of the corresponding rules for the propositional connective $\wedge$ (see Introduction, § 2).

(Ab1). By the definition of $\sqcap$ we have $a \sqcap (a \sqcup b) \leqslant a$. On the other hand, $a \leqslant a$ and $a \leqslant a \sqcup b$, hence $a \leqslant a \sqcap (a \sqcup b)$. The rules for $\sqcup$ are proved correspondingly.

Consequences

From (Ab) it follows, in fact without direct use of the order relation, that:

(F1) $$a \sqcap b = a \leftrightarrow a \sqcup b = b.$$

Proof. 1) From $a \sqcup b = b$ and (Ab1) it follows that $a \sqcap b = a$.

2) Let $a \sqcap b = a$. Then it follows from (Ab2) that

$$b \sqcup (b \sqcap a) = b, \text{ i.e. } b \sqcup a = b.$$

(F2) $$a \sqcap a = a, \quad a \sqcup a = a.$$

Proof. From (Ab2) it follows with $b = a$ that

$$a \sqcup (a \sqcap a) = a;$$

now it follows from (Ab1) with $b = a \sqcap a$ that

$$a = a \sqcap ((a \sqcap a) \sqcup a) = a \sqcap a.$$

$a \sqcup a = a$ is proved correspondingly.

For the connections between the order relation and the operation we have

(F3) $$a \leqslant b \leftrightarrow a \sqcap b = a \text{ (or } a \sqcup b = b).$$

Proof. 1) If $a \leqslant b$, then a satisfies the conditions by which $a \sqcap b$ is defined: $a \leqslant a \wedge a \leqslant b$ and if $c \leqslant a \wedge c \leqslant b$, then $c \leqslant a$.

2) From $a \sqcap b = a$ it follows that $a \leqslant b$, because $a \sqcap b \leqslant b$.

(F4) From $b \leqslant c$ it follows that $a \sqcap b \leqslant a \sqcap c$ and $a \sqcup b \leqslant a \sqcup c$.

Proof.
$a \sqcap b \leqslant a$ by definition
$a \sqcap b \leqslant b$ by definition
$a \sqcap b \leqslant c$ because $b \leqslant c$.

Hence $a \sqcap b \leqslant a \wedge a \sqcap b \leqslant c$, and so $a \sqcap b \leqslant a \sqcap c$.

From this it follows (with the help of the commutative law) that $a_1 \leqslant a_2 \wedge b_1 \leqslant b_2 \rightarrow a_1 \sqcap b_1 \leqslant a_2 \sqcap b_2 \wedge a_1 \sqcup b_1 \leqslant a_2 \sqcup b_2$.

Instead of defining a lattice by the order relation with the existence of *sup* and *inf* for any two elements, it can also be characterized by the operations $\sqcap$ and $\sqcup$ with the rules (C), (A), (Ab). For a more precise description of the facts we introduce the following notation due to Dedekind: If in a set V two operations $\top$, $\perp$ are defined[1] satisfying the rules

(K) $a \top b = b \top a, \qquad a \perp b = b \perp a,$

(A) $a \top (b \top c) = (a \top b) \top c, \quad a \perp (b \perp c) = (a \perp b) \perp c,$

(Ab) $a \top (a \perp b) = a, \qquad a \perp (a \top b) = a$

then we call $(V, \top, \perp)$ a *dual group*.

We have proved that if $(V, \leqslant)$ is a lattice and if we define

$$a \top b = a \sqcap b, \quad a \perp b = a \sqcup b,$$

(then $(V, \top, \perp)$), and hence $(V, \sqcap, \sqcup)$, is a dual group and we have

$$a \leqslant b \leftrightarrow a \top b = a.$$

If we define in $(V, \top, \perp)$ a relation $\lessapprox$ by

($\lessapprox$) $$a \lessapprox b \leftrightharpoons a \top b = a$$

then $(V, \lessapprox)$ is a lattice and we have

$$a \top b = a \sqcap b \text{ and } \perp a \; b = a \sqcup b \text{ and } a \lessapprox b \leftrightharpoons a \leqslant b.$$

[1] Here (and only here) the meaning of the symbols $\top$, $\perp$ differs from that introduced in Chapter I, § 3.

Specifically:

1) $\leqslant$ is reflexive.

Proof. Since (F2) follows from (C), (A), (Ab) alone, we have in $(V, \top, \perp)$ that

$$a \top a = a, \text{ hence } a \leqslant a.$$

2) $\leqslant$ is transitive.

Proof. Let (i) $a \leqslant b$, i.e. $a \top b = a$,

and (ii) $b \leqslant c$, i.e. $b \top c = b$.

Substitution of (ii) into (i) gives

$$a \top (b \top c) = a;$$

by the associative law

$$(a \top b) \top c = a$$

and by (i)

$$a \top c = a, \text{ i.e. } a \leqslant c.$$

3) $\leqslant$ is anti-symmetric.

Proof. Let $a \leqslant b$, i.e. $a \top b = a$

and $b \leqslant a$, i.e. $b \top a = b$.

Then it follows from the commutative law that $a=b$.

4) Existence of $a \sqcap b$. We claim that $a \sqcap b = a \top b$. What we have to prove is that $a \top b$ satisfies the conditions by which $a \sqcap b$ was defined, namely

(*i*) $a \top b \leqslant a$, (*ii*) $a \top b \leqslant b$, (*iii*) $x \leqslant a \wedge x \leqslant b \rightarrow x \leqslant a \top b$.

After translation by means of the definition ($\leqslant$) we have:

(*i*) $a \top (a \top b) = a \top b$. This follows from (A) and $a \top a = a$.

(*ii*) $b \top (a \top b) = a \top b$, similarly by using (C).

(*iii*) from $x \top a = x$ and $x \top b = x$ it follows that $\top\ x (a \top b) = = (x \top a) \top b = x \top b = x$,

as required.

The proof of the existence of $a \sqcup b$, in fact of $a \sqcup b = a \perp b$, can be left to the reader.

5) But now we have (F3)

$$a \leqslant b \leftrightarrow a \sqcap b = a.$$

We have proved

$$a \sqcap b = a \top b,$$

hence

$$a \leqslant b \leftrightarrow a \top b = a.$$

But this was the definition of $a \leqslant b$.

We have gone from the lattice $(V, \leqslant)$ to the dual group $(V, \top, \perp)$ and from there back to the lattice. But we can also start out from the dual group $(V, \top, \perp)$, define again a relation by $(\leqslant)$ and demonstrate that $(V, \leqslant)$ is a lattice. In fact, this is what we have just done. And since we have also shown that $a \sqcap b = a \top b$, $a \sqcup b = a \perp b$, we have proved that if we go over from $(V, \leqslant)$ again to the dual group $(V, \sqcap, \sqcap)$, we obtain the same dual group from which we started.

The only difficulty in these arguments is to see quite clearly *that* something has to be proved and *what* has to be proved; the actual proofs are almost trivial.

CHAPTER IV

Fundamental Concepts of Abstract Algebra

Between dual group and lattice there are conceptual differences, comparable roughly to the fact that an equi*lateral* triangle is conceptually not the same as an equi*angular* one. For a more detailed investigation of this difference and its consequences (concerning the concept sublattice see page 70) we shall now continue the discussion of general concepts begun in Chapter I.

§ 1. Formations

A set in which a system of relations is defined is called a *formation* (Chapter I, § 3). Here both the set and the relations have to be imagined as given explicitly.

1.1. Examples

The set of natural numbers with the relation $\underset{z}{\leqslant}$, both defined recursively: $(N, \underset{z}{\leqslant})$.

The set of rational numbers with addition, also defined recursively: $(\boldsymbol{Q}, +)$.

The set of real numbers with addition and multiplication: $(\boldsymbol{R}, +, \cdot)$.

The set of subsets of a set e with the relation $\subseteq$ (contained in) $(\mathfrak{P}e, \subseteq)$.

The set of subsets of a set e with the operations $\cap$, $\cup$: $(\mathfrak{P}e, \cap, \cup)$.

$\mathfrak{P}e$, with the operations $\cap$, $\cup$ and complementation, i.e. a binary relation that associates with an element x its complement x^0; this formation shall be denoted by $(\mathfrak{P}e, \cap, \cup, {}^0)$.

We have not yet specified that such a formation is a group, or a lattice, etc.; for this purpose a further concept is required.

With the concepts so far introduced the further concepts of homomorphism, isomorphism, and congruence relation are immediately accessible.

1.2. Homomorphism

Let $(M; R_1,\ldots,R_k)$ and $(M'; R'_1,\ldots,R'_k)$ be two formations. M and M', as well as the R_i and R'_i may, but need not, be distinct.

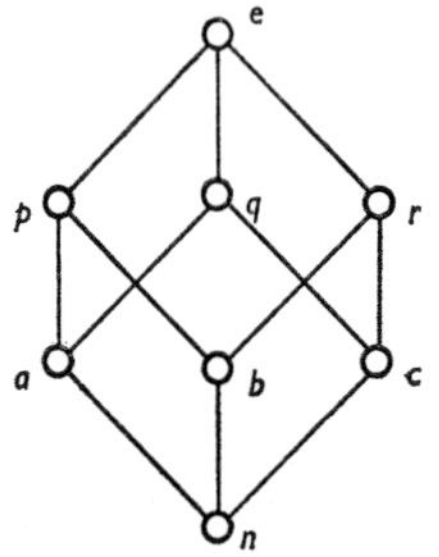

Fig. 14

Example 1. $M=\{n,a,b,c,p,q,r,e\}$. Suppose that in M the operations $\sqcap$, $\sqcup$ are defined according to the order diagram of Fig. 14.

$$\begin{aligned}
&R_1(x,y,z) \leftrightharpoons x \sqcap y = z\\
&R_2(x,y,z) \leftrightharpoons x \sqcup y = z\\
&M' = M\\
&R'_1(x,y,z) \leftrightharpoons x \sqcup y = z\\
&R'_2(x,y,z) \leftrightharpoons x \sqcap y = z.
\end{aligned}$$

Example 2.

$$\begin{aligned}
&M = \{n,a,b,c,e\}, \quad M' = \{n',p',q',e'\},\\
&R_1(x,y) \leftrightharpoons x \leqslant y,\\
&R'_1(x,y) \leftrightharpoons x \leqslant' y,
\end{aligned}$$

where $\leqslant$ and $\leqslant'$ are defined by the order diagrams of Fig. 15.

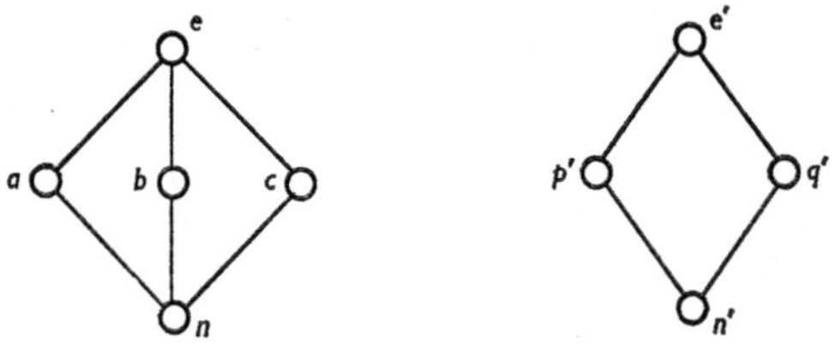

Fig. 15

A *homomorphism* consists of a mapping ψ of the R_i into the R'_j and a mapping φ of M into M'.

As to the mapping ψ, we postulate that it associates with every R_i precisely one $R'_j = \psi R_i$ and with every R'_j precisely one $R_i = \psi^{-1} R'_j$; here ψR_i is to contain as many variables as R_i. It is convenient to choose the numbering so that $\psi R_i = R'_i$; in the applications R_i and R'_i are frequently the same relations.

As to the mapping φ, we postulate that for all i and all x_ν

(1) $$R_i(x_1, \ldots, x_n) \rightarrow \psi R_i(\varphi x_1, \ldots, \varphi x_n)$$

If R_i and ψR_i are internal operations, then (1) becomes

$$f_i(x_1, \ldots, x_{n-1}) = y \rightarrow \psi f_i(\varphi x_1, \ldots, \varphi x_{n-1}) = \varphi y$$

or

(1a) $$\varphi(f_i(x_1, \ldots, x_{n-1})) = \psi f_i(\varphi x_1, \ldots, \varphi x_{n-1})$$

and for a binary internal operation $\top$ and its image $\top'$

(1b) $$\varphi(x \top y) = \varphi x \top' \varphi y.$$

For external operations, in addition, a mapping of the operator domains has to be taken into account. As a rule it is postulated that $\Omega_i = \Omega'_i$ and that the mapping $\Omega_i \rightarrow \Omega'_i$ is the identity, i.e. φ is subject to the postulate

(1c) $$\varphi(\omega \perp y) = \omega \perp' \varphi y.$$

If these conditions are satisfied, then (φ, ψ) is called a *homomorphism*. If the mapping ψ is evident, for example, by equal numbering $\psi R_i = R'_i$, then it is not mentioned specifically and the mapping φ alone is called a homomorphism.

In Example 1 the following table represents some of the possibilities for homomorphisms:

R	$\sqcap$ $\sqcup$	x	n	a	b	c	p	q	r	e
$\psi_1 R$	$\sqcap$ $\sqcup$	$\varphi_1 x$	n	a	b	c	p	q	r	e
$\psi_2 R$	$\sqcup$ $\sqcap$	$\varphi_2 x$	e	p	q	r	a	b	c	n
$\psi_3 R$	$\sqcup$ $\sqcap$	$\varphi_3 x$	e	r	q	p	c	b	a	n

In Example 2 the mapping of R_1 to R_1' is the only one possible. The table gives two possibilities for φx:

x	n	a	b	c	e
$\varphi_1 x$	n'	p'	p'	q'	e'
$\varphi_2 x$	n'	p'	q'	q'	e'

However, we shall apply the notion of *homomorphism* only when the two formations in question are 'of equal structure'. This expression will be defined in more detail in § 2; here we shall illustrate the fact in the example of ordered sets and lattices.

Suppose then that $(V, \leqslant)$, $(V', \leqslant')$ are ordered sets. In contrast to the general definition it is not only assumed that $\leqslant$ and $\leqslant'$ are binary relations, but that they are order relations, i.e. satisfy the laws (r), (t), (as) (Chapter II, § 1). A mapping $x \rightarrow x' = \varphi x$ satisfying

(0) $$x \leqslant y \rightarrow \varphi x \leqslant' \varphi y$$

is called *order homomorphism* or isotone or monotone mapping. The last name is customary, especially in the case when $M = M'$ is the set of real numbers and $\leqslant$ means the ordinary 'less than or equal'. $\leqslant'$ can also be defined as $\geqslant$; then φ is called a monotone decreasing function.

Now let $(V, \sqcap, \sqcup)$, $(V', \sqcap', \sqcup')$ be dual groups. A mapping $x \rightarrow \varphi x$ is called $\sqcap$-homomorphism if

(1) $$\varphi(x \sqcap y) = \varphi x \sqcap' \varphi y$$

Thus, it is quite permissible to restrict the concept of 'homomorphism' to a definite choice of relations.

If

(2) $$\varphi(x \sqcup y) = \varphi x \sqcup' \varphi y,$$

then φ is called $\sqcup$-homomorphism, and if both (1) and (2) hold, dual group homomorphism or lattice homomorphism.

Let us imagine the lattice $(V, \leqslant)$ characterized as a dual group $(V, \sqcap, \sqcup)$, and similarly $(V', \leqslant')$ as $(V', \sqcap', \sqcup')$. Then an order homomorphism need not be a $\sqcap$-homomorphism. This is shown by the example: $V = V' = \{1, 2, 3, 4, 6, 12\}$, i.e. the set of divisors of 12. We order it once according to divisibility and once in increasing magnitude (see Fig. 16). The mapping $x \rightarrow \varphi x = x$ is an order homomorphism of $(V, |)$ onto $(V', \leqslant)$, because $x|y \rightarrow x \leqslant y$.

True, we have here a bi-unique mapping of V onto $V' = V$, but the inverse mapping is not an order homomorphism; for $x \leqslant y \rightarrow x|y$ does not hold, for example, when $x = 2$, $y = 3$. The mapping is not a $\sqcap$-homomorphism; for $6 \sqcap 4$ is 2 in the order diagram on the left, 4 on the right. In general we have only:

from $x \sqcap y \leqslant x$ follows $\varphi(x \sqcap y) \leqslant \varphi x$

and from $x \sqcap y \leqslant y$ follows $\varphi(x \sqcap y) \leqslant \varphi y$.

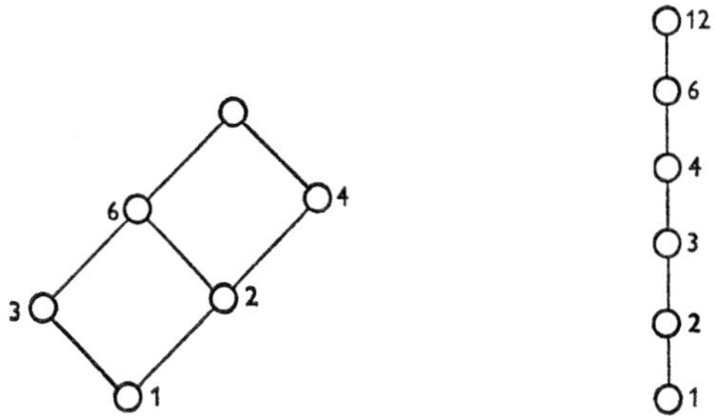

Fig. 16

Hence we have

$$(3\sqcap) \qquad \varphi(x \sqcap y) \leqslant \varphi x \sqcap \varphi y.$$

However, a $\sqcap$-homomorphism is always an order homomorphism, i.e. (0) follows from (1).

Proof. Let $x \leqslant y$; then $x = x \sqcap y$, hence by (1)

$$\varphi x = \varphi x \sqcap \varphi y, \text{ i.e. } \varphi x \leqslant \varphi y.$$

But a $\sqcap$-homomorphism is not always at the same time a $\sqcup$-homomorphism. True, from (1) follows (0) and consequently

from $x \leqslant x \sqcup y$ follows $\varphi x \leqslant \varphi(x \sqcup y)$,
from $y \leqslant x \sqcup y$ follows $\varphi y \leqslant \varphi(x \sqcup y)$,

hence

$$(3\sqcup) \qquad \varphi x \sqcup \varphi y \leqslant \varphi(x \sqcup y).$$

The fact that equality does not always hold is shown by the example of Fig. 17. Here we have (1) and (0), but not (2).

A homomorphism φ is called an *isomorphism* if it is a one-to-one mapping of M onto M' and if the inverse mapping is also a homomorphism.

The condition that the mapping of M is required to be onto M' is comparatively unimportant. If need be, one can consider instead of M' the image set φM.

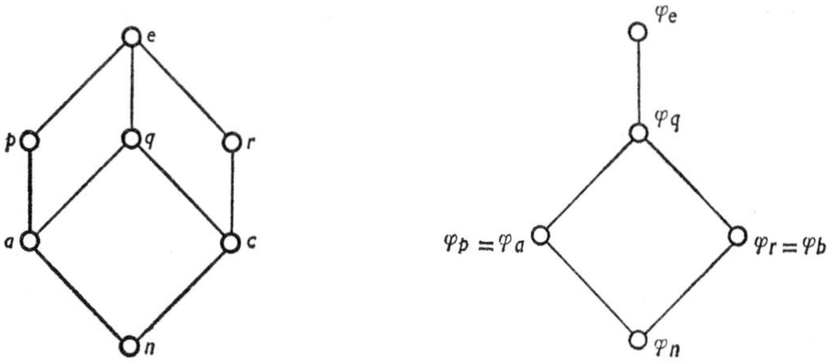

Fig. 17

From the bi-uniqueness it does not follow, in general, that the inverse mapping is also a homomorphism. This is shown by the example above of the divisors of 12. However, it does follow if the relations determining the homomorphism are operations. Let us carry out the proof for the operation $\sqcap$. It can be seen immediately that the proof is universally valid; one need only interpret the symbol $\sqcap$ as an arbitrary operation. It is assumed that φ is one-to-one, i.e. that the inverse mapping φ^{-1} exists. It is asserted that for arbitrary x', y' of V'

(4) $$\varphi^{-1}x' \sqcap \varphi^{-1}y' = \varphi^{-1}(x' \sqcap y').$$

Proof. Let $\varphi^{-1}x' = x$, $\varphi^{-1}y' = y$; then the left-hand side of the assertion is

$$x \sqcap y.$$

From

$$x' \sqcap y' = \varphi x \sqcap \varphi y = \varphi(x \sqcap y)$$

it follows also that

$$\varphi^{-1}(x' \sqcap y') = x \sqcap y.$$

Conversely, if the relation determining the homomorphism is an order relation, then the fact that the mapping φ is order homomorphic in both directions, i.e. that apart from (0) we have also

(5) $$\varphi x \leqslant \varphi y \rightarrow x \leqslant y,$$

allows us to deduce bi-uniqueness

$$\varphi x = \varphi y \leftrightarrow \varphi x \leqslant \varphi y \wedge \varphi y \leqslant \varphi x \leftrightarrow x \leqslant y \wedge y \leqslant x \leftrightarrow x = y.$$

Consequently:

A ⊓-isomorphism is at the same time an order isomorphism. For then φ^{-1} is also a ⊓-homomorphism, hence an order homomorphism; therefore we have

$$x' \leqslant y' \rightarrow \varphi^{-1}x' \leqslant \varphi^{-1}y',$$

but this is just (5).

Finally we can show that an order isomorphism is a ⊔-isomorphism. By assumption there exists z such that

$$\varphi x \sqcup \varphi y = \varphi z$$

then	$\varphi x \leqslant \varphi z,$	hence	$x \leqslant z$ by (5)
	$\varphi y \leqslant \varphi z,$	hence	$y \leqslant z.$
thus	$x \sqcup y \leqslant z,$	hence	$\varphi(x \sqcup y) \leqslant \varphi z = \varphi x \sqcup \varphi y.$

On the other hand, by (3⊔)

$$\varphi x \sqcup \varphi y \leqslant \varphi(x \sqcup y).$$

So we have shown, first of all, that an order isomorphism is a ⊔-homomorphism. Now the same proof need only be repeated for the inverse mapping φ^{-1}.

Whereas in a lattice order homomorphism asserts less than ⊓-homomorphism, and this less than dual group homomorphism (for both operations), the corresponding isomorphisms are all equivalent.

A homomorphism φ of a formation $(M, R_1, \ldots, R_k)$ into itself, i.e. with $\varphi M \subseteq M$, $\varphi R_i = R_i$, is called an *endomorphism*; an isomorphism of a formation onto itself is an *automorphism.*

To be proved by the reader: the automorphisms of a formation (with successive application as the operation) for a group, the automorphism group of the formation.

An example of an endomorphism in the lattice of divisors of 12 is the mapping

x	1	2	4	3	6	12
φx	1	2	4	1	2	4

In fact, this is an order endomorphism as well as a ⊓- and ⊔-endomorphism.

Examples of automorphisms are obtained from lattices whose order diagram has a vertical axis of symmetry, by reflection in this axis, for example, in Fig. 14, page 60.

x	n	a	b	c	p	q	r	e
φx	n	c	b	a	r	q	p	e

1.3. Congruence relations

We shall define congruence relations only for operational formations $(M, R_1, \ldots, R_k)$ or $(M, f_1, \ldots, f_k)$, respectively (see Chapter I, § 3).

Definition. An equivalence relation ϱ is said to be *compatible* with the operation $f(x_1, \ldots, x_n) = u$ if

(1a) $$\bigwedge_{\nu=1}^{n} x_\nu \,\varrho\, y_\nu \rightarrow f(x_1, \ldots, x_n) \,\varrho\, f(y_1, \ldots, y_n).$$

For a binary internal operation (1a) becomes

(1b) $$x_1 \,\varrho\, y_1 \wedge x_2 \,\varrho\, y_2 \rightarrow (x_1 \top x_2) \,\varrho\, (y_1 \top y_2).$$

For a binary external operation the condition of compatibility is

(1c) $$x \,\varrho\, y \rightarrow (\omega \perp x) \,\varrho\, (\omega \perp y) \text{ for all } \omega, x, y.$$

An equivalence relation that is compatible with all the defining operations of a formation is called a *congruence relation* or briefly, a *congruence.*

Connection with homomorphisms

An equivalence ϱ generates a partition of M into classes: every x of M is associated with the class $\kappa x = \{v; x \,\varrho\, v\}$. We have

(2) $$\kappa x = \kappa y \leftrightarrow x \,\varrho\, y.$$

These classes are called equivalence classes or residue classes mod ϱ. We combine them into a set κM. κ is a mapping of M into the power set $\mathfrak{P}M$, more accurately of M onto $\kappa M \subseteq \mathfrak{P}M$.

Now we define in κM operations that correspond to the operations in M and are therefore denoted by the same symbols:

(3a) $$f_i(\kappa x_1, \ldots, \kappa x_n) \leftrightharpoons \kappa f_i(x_1, \ldots, x_n).$$

For a binary internal operation this becomes

(3b) $$\kappa x_1 \top \kappa x_2 \leftrightharpoons \kappa(x_1 \top x_2);$$

for a binary external operation we have to define:

(3b) $$\omega \perp \kappa x \leftrightharpoons \kappa(\omega \perp x).$$

It has to be shown that in this way operations in κM are well defined, i.e. that (T) and (E)—see Chapter I, § 3—are satisfied. That (T) holds is clear. The assertion (E) in slightly modified form reads

(4) $$\bigwedge_{\nu=1}^{n} \kappa x_\nu = \kappa y_\nu \rightarrow f_i(\kappa x_1, \ldots, \kappa x_n) = f_i(\kappa y_1, \ldots, \kappa y_n);$$

in other words, the values of the f_i must depend on the classes only and not on the accidentally chosen 'representatives'.

Proof of (4). (We abbreviate $f_i(x_1, \ldots, x_n)$ by $f_i(x_\nu)$.)

From	$\kappa x_\nu = \kappa y_\nu$	follows	$x_\nu \varrho y_\nu$	by (2);
from	$\bigwedge_\nu x_\nu \varrho y_\nu$	follows	$f_i(x_\nu) \varrho f_i(y_\nu)$	by (1a),
hence	$\kappa f_i(x_\nu) = \kappa f_i(y_\nu)$			by (2)
and so	$f_i(\kappa x_\nu) = f_i(\kappa y_\nu)$			by (3a).

Equations (3) characterize the mapping κ as a homomorphism. Thus, every congruence relation is associated with a homomorphism.

Conversely, to every homomorphism φ there corresponds a congruence relation ϱ, namely the one defined by

(5) $$x \varrho y \leftrightharpoons \varphi x = \varphi y.$$

That ϱ is reflexive and comparable is easily seen. The compatibility of ϱ with the operations f_i, i.e. (1a), is proved as follows:

From $x_\nu \varrho y_\nu$ follows	$\varphi x_\nu = \varphi y_\nu$	by (5)
hence	$f_i(\varphi x_\nu) = f_i(\varphi y_\nu)$,	
hence	$\varphi f_i(x_\nu) = \varphi f_i(y_\nu)$	by (3a),
hence	$f_i(x_\nu) \varrho f_i(y_\nu)$	by (5).

§ 2. Structure

So far in the preceding section we have thought of the set M and the relations $R_1, \ldots$ as given explicitly. But on occasion we have discussed properties of relations and so have characterized classes of relations. An example occurred in the form

$$\bigwedge_x \bigwedge_y \bigwedge_z (R(y,x) \wedge R(y,z) \rightarrow R(x,z)).$$

We have also specified systems of relations in such a way that, for example, they characterized a dual group. Consider, for instance, the absorption law

$$\bigwedge_a \bigwedge_b a \sqcap (a \sqcup b) = a;$$

by means of the relations

$$R_1(x,y,z) \leftrightarrows x \sqcap y = z, \quad R_2(x,y,z) \leftrightarrows x \sqcup y = z$$

it can be written thus:

$$\bigwedge_a \bigwedge_b \bigwedge_c R_2(a,b,c) \rightarrow R_1(a,c,a).$$

Such a law has the following forms: certain 'object variables' $a, b, c, x, y\ldots$ and variables for predicates $R_1,\ldots,R_k$ are available. $R_1(x_1,\ldots,x_{n1}),\ldots,R_k(x_1,\ldots,x_{nk})$ will be called primitive predicates. By means of the connectives $\wedge, \vee, \neg$ (non), $\rightarrow$, as well as the quantifiers $\bigwedge_x, \bigvee_x$ propositions are formed (in which all object variables are bound, but the obvious binding of the free variables by $\bigwedge$ is not always written down explicitly). Such a system of propositions is called an *axiom system* (Σ).

If now $\mathfrak{M}=(M,R_1,\ldots,R_k)$ is a formation and if the propositions of an axiom system become true propositions when the relations of $\mathfrak{M}$ are substituted for the propositional variables and the domain of variability for the object variables is taken as the set M, then $\mathfrak{M}$ is called a *model* for the axiom system Σ.

If Σ' is logically equivalent to Σ, but with the same predicate variables $R_1,\ldots,R_k$, then obviously every model of Σ is also a model of Σ'. We call a class of logically equivalent axiom systems a fine structure; if $\mathfrak{M}$ is a model of Σ, then we say: $\mathfrak{M}$ carries the fine structure Σ (the fine structure can be denoted by an arbitrary one of the equivalent axiom systems).

The terms 'lattice' and 'dual groups' are names for fine structures. This example shows that for fine structures there is still an equivalence which can be described in the general case as follows: let Σ be an axiom system for the relation R_κ, $\kappa=1,\ldots,k$ (for example, that of a dual group with $R_1(x,y,z) \leftrightarrows x \sqcap y=z$, $R_2(x,y,z) \leftrightarrows x \sqcup y=z$). With the help of the R_κ certain propositions $R^*_\lambda \leftrightharpoons \mathsf{P}^*_\lambda\ (R_1,\dots,R_k)$ are formed (for example, $R^*(x,y) \leftrightharpoons R_1(x,y,x)$, hence $x \leqslant y \leftrightharpoons x \sqcap y = x$). Suppose that Σ^* is a system of propositions containing only the R^*_λ but not the R_κ, and that Σ^* is a consequence of Σ. Suppose that it is also possible to represent the R_κ by the R^*_λ (in our example: $R_1(x,y,z) \leftrightarrow R^*(z,x) \wedge R^*(z,y)$

$$\wedge \bigwedge_w (R^*(w,x) \wedge R^*(w,y) \rightarrow R^*(w,z)),$$

and that then Σ follows from Σ^*. In this case we say: $\Sigma^*(R^*_\lambda)$ and $\Sigma(R_\kappa)$ determine the same *structure*. In this sense 'lattice' is used as a *structural* concept. In spite of this equivalence the concept of a fine structure cannot be omitted; we have already seen that the concept of homomorphism depends essentially on the basic relations; it also shows up in the concept of *sub-formation* which is to be defined with reference to the fine structure.

Suppose that $\mathfrak{M} = (M; R_1,\dots,R_k)$ is a formation carrying the fine structure Σ and that $N \subseteq M$. If R_κ is an n_κ-ary relation, i.e. $R_\kappa \subseteq M \times \dots \times M \leftrightharpoons M^{n_\kappa}$, then let $R'_\kappa \leftrightharpoons R_\kappa \cap N^{n_\kappa}$ be the relation *induced* by R_κ in N. In most cases we can denote it again by R_κ. If the same axioms Σ hold for the formation $\mathfrak{N} = (N; R'_1,\dots,R'_k)$, then $\mathfrak{N}$ is called a *sub-formation of* $\mathfrak{M}$ *relative to* Σ.

Whether validity of Σ in $\mathfrak{M}$ implies validity in $\mathfrak{N}$ depends on the logical form of the axioms. We take it as a fact of logic that every proposition can be transformed so that all quantifiers stand, without negation, at the beginning and that their domains of action extend to the end of the formula. This form is called *prenex normal form*. (In (Q4) on page 22 the left-hand side is in this form.)

If a proposition in the prenex form contains only $\bigwedge$-quantifiers and if it holds in M, then it evidently holds in every subset of M. An example of this form is the axiom system that characterizes $(M, \leqslant)$ as an ordered set.

If R is, say, a binary relation, then Σ also contains the assertions of uniqueness

(E) $$\bigwedge_x \bigwedge_y \bigwedge_z \bigwedge_{z'} (R(x,y,z) \wedge R(x,y,z') \rightarrow z = z')$$

which carry over from M to $N \subseteq M$, and of left totality

(T) $$\bigwedge_x \bigwedge_y \bigvee_z R(x,y,z) \quad \text{or} \quad \bigwedge_x \bigwedge_y \bigvee_z f(x,y) = z, \ \text{respectively},$$

whose validity does not pass from M to N since it can happen that there is a z in M but no z in N (for a given x, y in N). If

$$\bigwedge_{x\in N}\ \bigwedge_{y\in N}\ \bigvee_{z\in N} R(x,y,z) \quad \text{or} \quad \bigwedge_{x\in N}\ \bigwedge_{y\in N}\ \bigvee_{z\in N} f(x,y)=z \text{ respectively,}$$

then N is said to be *closed relative to the operation* R or f, respectively.

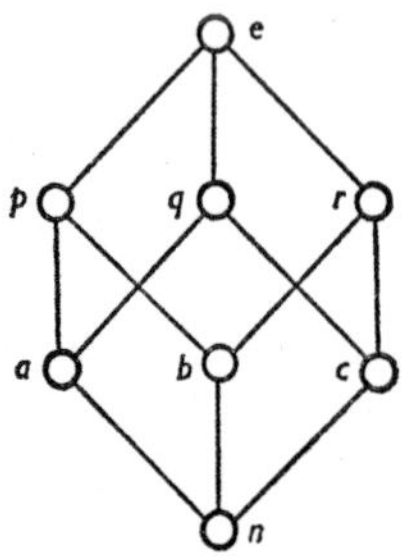

Fig. 18. 1

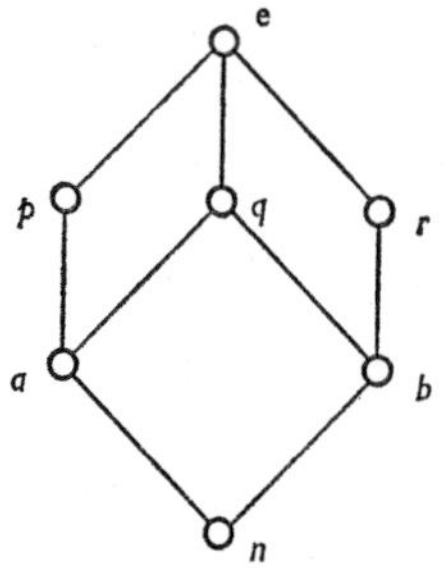

Fig. 18. 2

Example. Suppose that an order is given in the set

$$M = \{n, a, b, c, p, q, r, e\}$$

by the diagram of Fig. 18, 1. Obviously $(M, \leqslant)$ is a lattice. Let the operations $\sqcap, \sqcup$ defined by the order be fixed in a table so that they can now be regarded as given by the table, independently of the order. This table would contain $p \sqcap r = b$, among others. The subset $N = M - \{b\}$, which arises from M by omitting the element b, is not closed relative to the operation $\sqcap$ fixed by the table, because $p \sqcap r \notin N$.

Nevertheless, $(N, \leqslant)$ is a lattice. For every pair of elements of N there exists a greatest common lower element, but $\mathit{inf}(p,r) = n$; the operation *inf* in N is different from $\mathit{inf}\,(=\sqcap)$ in M.

More generally, let $(M, \leqslant)$ be a lattice, $(M, \sqcap, \sqcup)$ the dual group determined by $\leqslant$, and $N \subseteq M$.

If N is closed relative to $\sqcap$ and $\sqcup$, then $(N, \sqcap, \sqcup)$ is a sub-formation of $(M, \sqcap, \sqcup)$; for the remaining statements of the axiom system of a dual group contain in the prenex form only $\wedge$-quantifiers. In this case $(N, \sqcap, \sqcup)$ is called a *sub-lattice* of $(M, \sqcap, \sqcup)$—although sub-dual group would be preferable.

But if one only knows that $(N, \leqslant)$ is a lattice without knowing whether *inf* or *sup* in N is equal to *inf* or *sup* in M, then $(N, \leqslant)$ is called a *sub-formation* of $(M, \leqslant)$—although sub-lattice would be preferable.

A proposition that holds for the connective formation $(M; R_1, \ldots, R_k)$ and all its closed subsets is said to be *restriction-hereditary.* A proposition containing in its prenex form only $\bigwedge$-quantifiers and no $\bigvee$-quantifiers is restriction hereditary.

If one defines a group $(e, \cdot)$ by the postulate that $\cdot$ is an operation for which

$$\bigwedge_x \bigwedge_y \bigwedge_z (xy)z = x(yz),$$

$$\bigvee_e \bigwedge_x ex = xe = x, \quad \bigwedge_x \bigvee_y xy = yx = e,$$

then this axiom system contains $\bigvee$-quantifiers. And in fact, not every subset closed under multiplication is a subgroup.

Example. In the group of integers under addition the subset of positive integers is closed, but not a subgroup.

We shall show that *the set of sub-formations* of a formation $(M, R_1, \ldots, R_n)$ relative to a given axiom system Σ that satisfies a condition yet to be formulated *forms a complete lattice.*

Σ is said to be *intersection-hereditary* if the intersection of sub-formations N_i, i.e. $D = \bigcap_{i \in I} N_i$, is again a sub-formation. At any rate the following is clear: if all the N_i are closed with respect to the connecting operations, then so is D. We shall prove this incidentally.

1) If a proposition contains in its prenex form only $\bigwedge$-quantifiers and holds for a set N_i, then it holds in every subset, in particular in D; because D is a subset of every N_i.

2) If a proposition $\mathfrak{A}$ contains in its prenex form a $\bigvee$-quantifier, e.g.

$$\mathfrak{A} \leftrightharpoons \bigwedge_x \bigwedge_e \bigvee_y R(x, e, y),$$

it may nevertheless be intersection hereditary, as is shown, for example, by the second and third group axioms; this will be so, for example, if for every statement with $\bigvee_e$ the corresponding uniqueness statement, in the example $\mathfrak{A}$ above: the statement

$$\bigwedge_x \bigwedge_e \bigwedge_{e'} \bigwedge_y (R(x, e, y) \wedge R(x, e', y) \rightarrow e = e')$$

occurs in Σ or follows from Σ.

It is claimed that

$$\bigwedge_{x\in D} \bigvee_{e\in D} \bigwedge_{y\in D} R(x,e,y),$$

if the corresponding statement holds for all N_i (instead of D).

Proof. Let $x \in D$, hence $x \in N_i$ (for some $i \in I$); then we have

$$\bigvee_{e_i\in N_i} \bigwedge_{y\in N_i} R(x,e_i,y);$$

this also holds for all $y \in D$.

However, x is also an element of every other N_j; hence there is an $e_j \in N_j$ with

$$\bigwedge_{y\in D} R(x,e_j,y).$$

But from $R(x,e_i,y)$ and $R(x,e_j,y)$ it follows that $e_i = e_j$. Hence there is an e contained in all N_i, i.e. in D.

Now we have: for all formations with intersection-hereditary structure Σ the sub-formations form a complete lattice relative to inclusion.

For every non-empty set of sub-formations has an infimum, which is again a sub-formation relative to Σ, namely the intersection

$$\bigcap_{i\in I} N_i = \bigsqcap_{i\in I} N_i.$$

Furthermore, every family of subsets has an upper bound, namely M itself. So it has an upper limit, by the theorem of the upper limit (Chapter II, § 2.2).

This theorem illustrates the importance of lattice theory. Birkhoff deems it of parallel standing with the theorem that the automorphisms of a formation form a group.

The converse holds, in general, only if one extends the notion of formation in such a way that one admits also infinitely many (this is not so bad; but also) infinitary relations.

CHAPTER V

Semi-modular and Modular Lattices

§ 1. The chain theorem

A chain L is called a *refinement* of the chain K if all the elements of K belong to L; a *proper refinement* if at least one element of L does not belong to K. A chain is called *maximal* if it is a proper chain and there are no proper refinements of it. In finite chains this means that the terms of the chain are neighbours.

We ask what conditions on a lattice are sufficient for all finite maximal chains between two fixed elements to have the same length, more accurately, for the *Dedekind Chain Theorem* to hold:

If between two elements a, b there is a maximal chain of finite length l, then every maximal finite chain between a and b has the length l. We call $l(a,b)$ the distance from a to b.

First of all a special case: if a is a lower neighbour of x and x a lower neighbour of b and if the chain theorem holds, then a second finite chain $a<y<b$ can contain only one intermediary element. This is illustrated in Fig. 19, which suggests the following definition:

> A lattice is called *lower semi-modular* if any two elements x and y having a common upper neighbour ($b=x \sqcup y$) also have a common lower neighbour ($a=x \sqcap y$).

The concept *upper semi-modular* is defined analogously; the definition (for example, for upper semi-modular) can also be stated as follows:

> If $x \sqcap y$ is a lower neighbour of x and of y, then $x \sqcup y$ is an upper neighbour of x and of y.

The chain theorem does not imply semi-modularity, as the example of Fig. 20 shows. But if the chain theorem holds for a lattice and all its sub-lattices, then the lattice is upper and lower semi-modular (we omit the proof). In our example the chain theorem does not hold for the sub-lattice that arises by omission of the element encircled twice.

However, the converse holds: *if a lattice is lower (or upper) semi-modular, then the chain theorem holds.*

The proof is by mathematical induction. If there is a chain of length 2 between a and b, then every other finite chain between a and b has the length 2. This is an immediate consequence of the definition of semi-modularity.

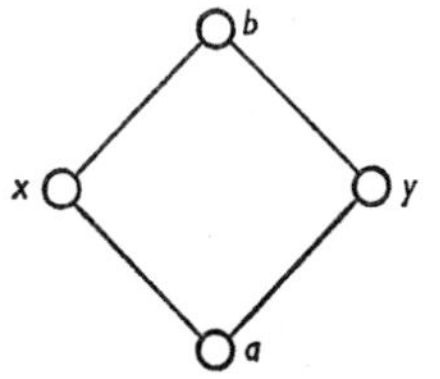

Fig. 19

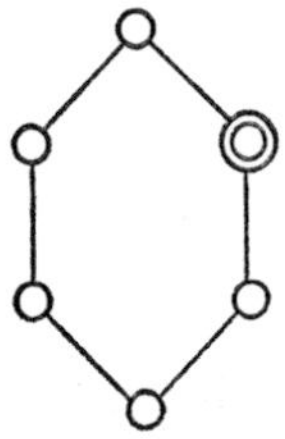

Fig. 20

We now assume that our theorem holds for chains of length less than l and prove it for chains of length l. Let

$$K_1: \qquad b = x_0 > x_1 > \ldots > x_{l-1} > x_l = a,$$

$$K_2: \qquad b = y_0 > y_1 > \ldots > y_{m-1} > y_m = a$$

be two maximal chains between a and b. If $x_1 = y_1$, then the statement follows immediately from the inductive hypothesis. If $x_1 \neq y_1$, then they have the common upper neighbour b, hence a common lower neighbour z_2. It can happen that $z_2 = x_2$. We now construct a maximal chain between z_2 and a. If $z_2 = x_2$, then $x_2 > x_3 > \ldots > a$ is one of them; otherwise z_2 and x_2 have the common upper neighbour x_1, hence a common lower neighbour z_3, possibly $z_3 = x_3$. In this way we continue. Since $a \leqslant z_i$ for all i, the construction stops after finitely many steps.

The example of Fig. 21 should convince the reader that this attention to detail is necessary. In this example R is the set of rational numbers between 0 and 1 with the order relation $\leqslant_z$. The lattice with this order diagram is both upper and lower semi-modular, and the chain theorem holds in the formulation given above, although in the sub-lattice $(R, \underset{z}{\leqslant})$ there are neither neighbours nor finite maximal chains.

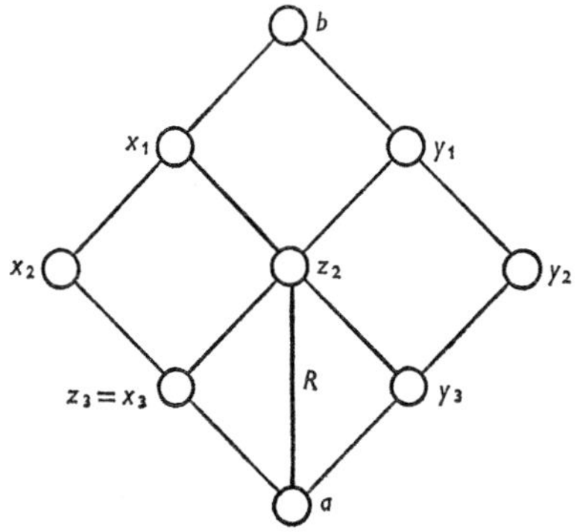

Fig. 21

Now the chain

	$x_1 > z_2 > \dots > a$	is of length $l-1$,
	$z_2 > \dots > a$	of length $l-2$,
	$y_1 > z_2 > \dots > a$	of length $l-1$,
hence also	$y_1 > y_2 > \dots > a$	is of length $l-1$,
and so	$b > y_1 > \dots > a$	is of length l.

The Dedekind Chain Theorem is a consequence of semi-modularity.

The definition of semi-modularity given so far is only suitable for 'discrete' lattices. In order to find another formulation we start out from the lattice $(\bar{m})$ (Fig. 22. 1) which is obviously the simplest non-semi-modular lattice. To describe the order diagram we note

(1) $$a \sqcap b < c < a < c \sqcup b.$$

What elements must be adjoined to give rise to a semi-modular lattice? First of all, to make the chain theorem valid we adjoin an element t such that

$$b < t < b \sqcup c.$$

Now if we want any two elements which have a common upper neighbour also to have a common lower neighbour we must adjoin $a \sqcap t$. If we were to choose $a \sqcap t = c$ or $a \sqcap t = b$, we would no longer have $a < c \sqcup b$. Hence we have no option but to choose $a \sqcap t$ as in the figure; this position can also be specified by writing $(a \sqcap t) \sqcup c = a$.

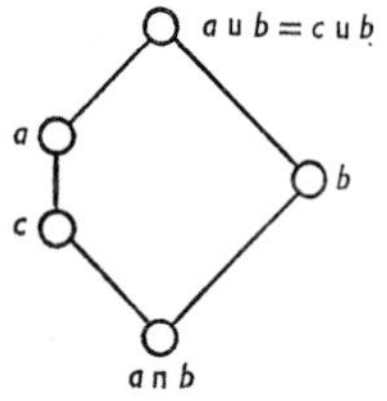

Fig. 22. 1 ($\bar{m}$)

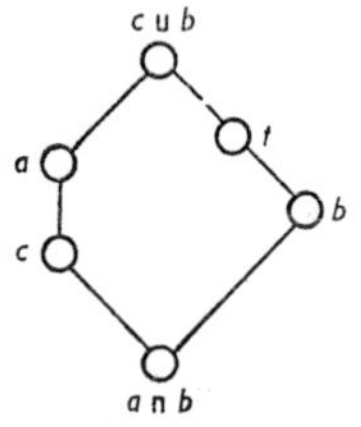

Fig. 22. 2

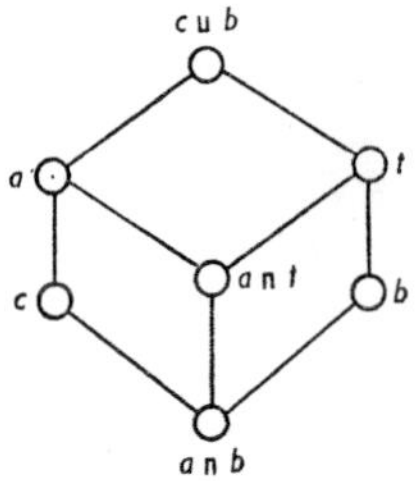

Fig. 22. 3

This argument, which makes no claim to rigour, is merely meant to motivate the following definition:

(lsm): $(V, \leqslant)$ is called *strictly lower semi-modular* if

(1) $$a \sqcap b < c < a < c \sqcup b$$

always implies that

(2) $$\bigvee_t (b < t < b \sqcup c \wedge (a \sqcap t) \sqcup c = a).$$

The concepts of 'upper neighbour' and 'lower neighbour' are now no longer used.

(usm): $(V, \leqslant)$ is called *strictly upper semi-modular* if (1) implies

(2′) $$\bigvee_s (a \sqcap b < s < b \wedge (c \sqcup s) \sqcap a = c).$$

Every strictly (lower) semi-modular lattice is (lower) semi-modular in the sense of page 73.

Proof. We assume that a and b have a common upper neighbour $a \sqcup b$ and prove that $a \sqcap b$ is a lower neighbour of a and b. In fact we shall prove that (*) $a \sqcap b < c < a$ leads to a contradiction.

Firstly, by combination with b it follows that:

$$b = (a \sqcap b) \sqcup b \leqslant c \sqcup b \leqslant a \sqcup b.$$

Now the following cases are possible:

1) $$b = c \sqcup b.$$

But then $c \leqslant b$ and since also $c \leqslant a$, we would have $c \leqslant a \sqcap b$ in contradiction to (*).

2) $b < c \sqcup b < a \sqcup b$; this is in contradiction to the fact that $a \sqcup b$ is an upper neighbour of b.

3) $c \sqcup b = a \sqcup b$. Then it follows from (lsm) that there exists a t between b and $c \sqcup b = a \sqcup b$, again in contradiction to the fact that $a \sqcup b$ is an upper neighbour of b.

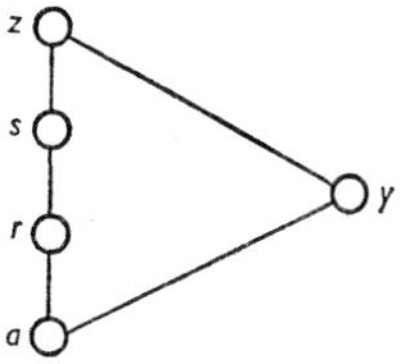

Fig. 23

However, not every (lower) semi-modular lattice is also strictly semi-modular. This is shown by the example of Fig. 21, page 75, part of which is drawn in Fig. 23. Here we have

$$s \sqcap y < r < s < r \sqcup y,$$

but there is no t between y and $r \sqcup y$.

§ 2. Distance and dimension

Let $(V, \leqslant)$ be (upper) semi-modular and of bounded finite length. Then all maximal chains between two elements u and v have the same length $l(u, v)$. The elements $x \in V$ with $u \leqslant x \leqslant v$ form a sub-lattice of V. It is called the *interval* $v/u \leftrightharpoons \{x; u \leqslant x \leqslant v\}$. By l every interval v/u is associated with a natural number, which is zero only when $v = u$. If $u \leqslant v \leqslant w$, then $l(w/u) = l(w/v) + l(v/u)$.

We call $l(v/u)$ the *distance* between the elements u and v. In particular, if (Fig. 24) $v = a \sqcup b$, $u = a \sqcap b$, then

$$\begin{aligned} l(v/u) &= l(a \sqcup b/a) + l(a/a \sqcap b) \\ &= l(a \sqcup b/b) + l(b/a \sqcap b). \end{aligned}$$

What is the relationship between the lengths of 'opposite' chains, such as $l(a \sqcup b/a)$ and $l(b/a \sqcap b)$?

Let A: $a \sqcap b = a_0 < a_1 < \ldots < a_k = a$,

B: $a \sqcap b = b_0 < b_1 < \ldots < b_m = b$

be two maximal chains. We imagine that the chain B undergoes a 'parallel' shift along the chain A and ask in what way its length changes. More accurately: we form the chain (see Fig. 25)

C: $c_i = a_1 \sqcup b_i$.

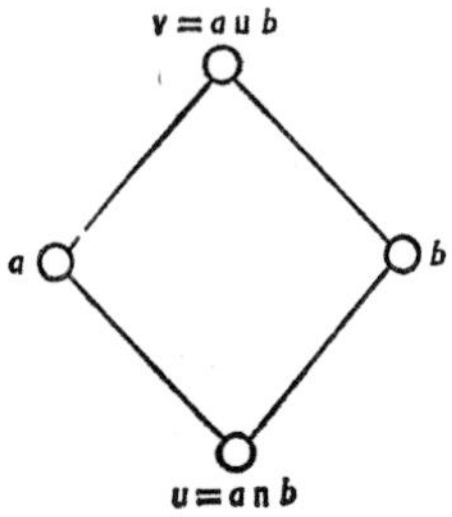

Fig. 24

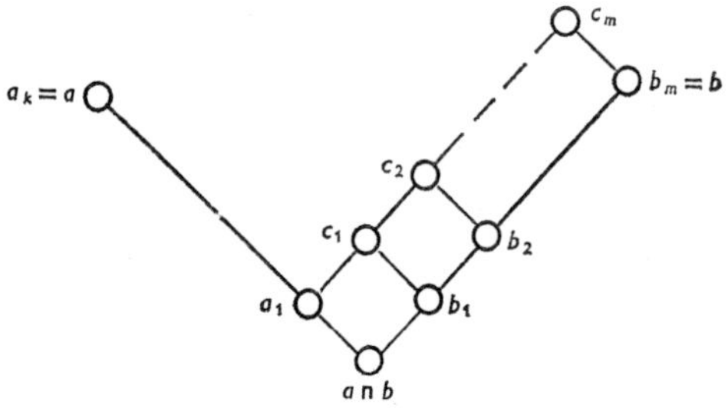

Fig. 25

Since a_1 and b_1 have a common lower neighbour $a \sqcap b$, c_1 is an upper neighbour of a_1 and b_1. Now $c_1 \neq a_2$ and $c_1 \neq b_2$; because quite generally

$$c_i = a_1 \sqcup b_i = a_j$$

leads to

$$b_i \leqslant a_j \leqslant a,$$
$$b_i \leqslant b,$$

and so the the contradiction

$$b_i \leqslant a \sqcap b$$

and $c_i = a_1 \sqcup b_i = b_j$ leads to the contradiction $a_1 \leqslant a \sqcap b$.

Furthermore, c_1 and b_2 then have a common upper neighbour $c_1 \sqcup b_2 = a_1 \sqcup b_1 \sqcup b_2 = a_1 \sqcup b_2 = c_2$ etc. up to c_m.

This shift of the maximal chain

$$b_0 < b_1 < \ldots < b_m = b$$

into $$a_1 = c_0 < c_1 < \ldots < c_m = b \sqcup a_1$$

has therefore left the length of the chain unaltered.

At the next step, $c'_i = c_i \sqcup a_2$, it remains true that

$c'_i = a_j$ leads to $\quad b_i \leqslant c_i \leqslant c'_i \leqslant a$,

and so to the contradiction $\quad b_i \leqslant a \sqcap b$,

but from $c'_i = c_j$ it only follows that $a_2 \leqslant b \sqcup a_1$, and not $a_2 \leqslant b$.

Since c_i' is an upper neighbour of c_i, we have to take the following possibility into account (Figs. 26 and 27):

$$c_1' \neq c_1, \ldots, c_{i-1}' \neq c_{j-1}, c_j' = c_{j+1}.$$

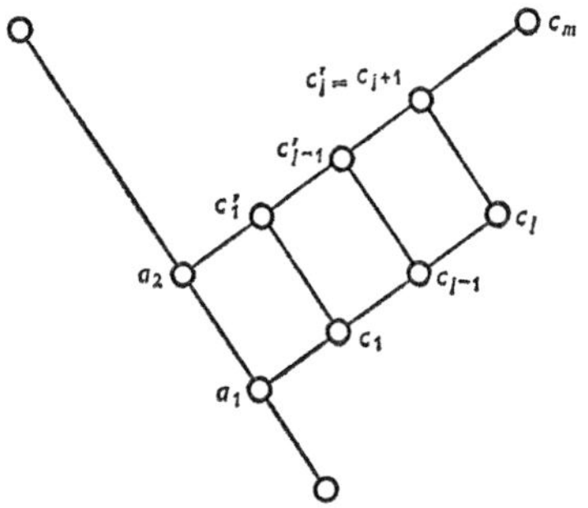

Fig. 26

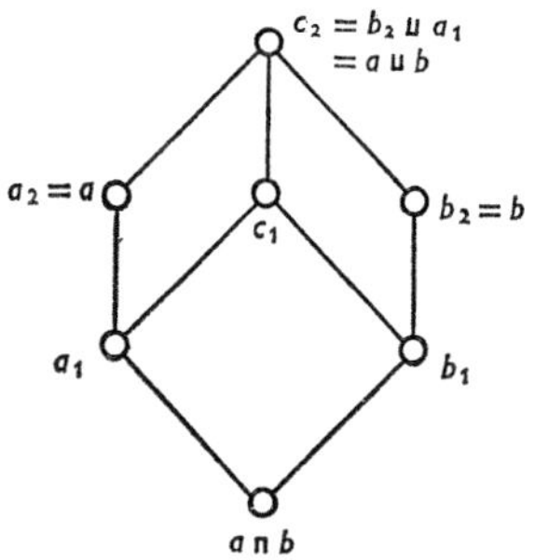

Fig. 27

But then it is easy to see that the chain

$$a_2 < c_1 < \ldots < c_j < c_{j+1} < \ldots < c_m$$

transforms into the chain

$$a_2 < c_1' < \ldots < c_{j-1}' < c_{j+1} < \ldots < c_m,$$

so that its length is decreased by 1. From this it follows: if $(V, \leqslant)$ is upper semi-modular, then

(1) $$l(a \sqcup b/a) \leqslant l(b/a \sqcap b).$$

Similarly one proves:

(2) $$(\text{lsm}) \rightarrow l(a \sqcup b/a) \geqslant l(b/a \sqcap b).$$

Therefore, if $(V, \leqslant)$ is of bounded finite length and semi-modular in both directions, then

(3) $$l(a \sqcup b/a) = l(b/a \sqcap b).$$

If $(V, \leqslant)$ is of finite length below and has therefore a zero element, then one calls

$$l(x, n) \leftrightharpoons \delta(x)$$

the *dimension of* x. Since for $u \leqslant v$

$$l(v/u) = \delta(v) - \delta(u)$$

(3) turns into the *dimension equation*

(4) $$\delta(a \sqcup b) - \delta(a) = \delta(b) - \delta(a \sqcap b)$$

or

$$\delta(a) + \delta(b) = \delta(a \sqcup b) + \delta(a \sqcap b).$$

For later applications we note

(5) $$a \leqslant b \wedge \delta(a) = \delta(b) \rightarrow a = b.$$

§ 3. Modularity

In the proof of the inequality for lengths (§ 2 (1) and (2)) we mapped the chain

$$a \sqcap b = a_0 < \ldots < a_m = a.$$

By the mapping φ,

$$\varphi x = b \sqcup x,$$

onto the chain $(a \sqcap b) \sqcup b = b < \ldots < a \sqcup b$. More generally, φ defines an order homomorphism of the interval $a/a \sqcap b$ into the interval $a \sqcup b/b$. Correspondingly, by

$$\psi y = a \sqcap y$$

an order homomorphism is defined of $a \sqcup b/b$ into $a/a \sqcap b$ (Fig. 28). If ψ is the inverse mapping of φ, then both mappings are isomorphisms.

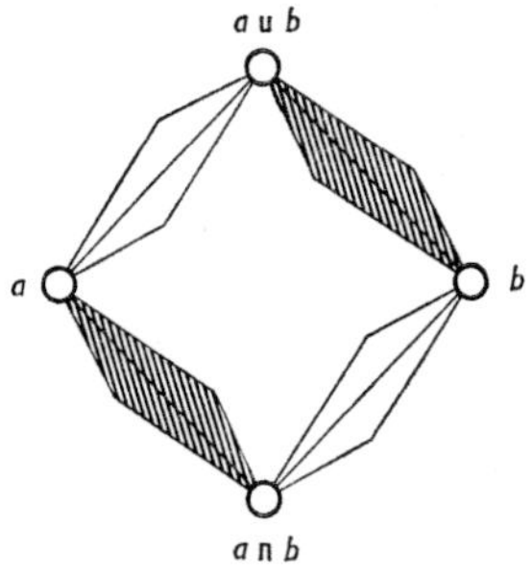

Fig. 28

In other words: it suffices for the existence of an isomorphic mapping of $a \sqcup b/b$ onto $a/a \sqcap b$ that for all $x \in a/a \sqcap b$ and all $y \in a \sqcup b/b$ we have

$$\psi\varphi x = x \text{ and } \varphi\psi y = y, \text{ i.e.}$$

(m1) $$a \sqcap b \leqslant x \leqslant a \rightarrow a \sqcap (b \sqcup x) = x,$$

(m1′) $$a \sqcup b \geqslant y \geqslant b \rightarrow b \sqcup (a \sqcap y) = y.$$

A lattice in which (m1) holds for all a, b, x is called *modular* and (m1) is called the *modular law*. We shall show later that in a modular lattice (m1′) also holds for all a, b, y.

That the modular law is not a consequence of the lattice axioms is shown by the example ($\bar{m}$) (Fig. 7. 8; page 47). The lattice axioms merely imply the *modular inequality*

$$x \leqslant a \rightarrow a \sqcap (b \sqcup x) \geqslant x,$$

for we have ($a \geqslant x$ and) $b \sqcup x \geqslant x$. To prove (m1), therefore, we only have to show

(m1u) $$a \sqcap b \leqslant x \leqslant a \rightarrow a \sqcap (b \sqcup x) \leqslant x.$$

(m1) can also be written in such a way that the assumption $a \sqcap b \leqslant x$ disappears. If $c \leqslant a$, then $x = (a \sqcap b) \sqcup c$ satisfies the condition $a \sqcap b \leqslant x \leqslant a$, hence it follows from (m1), because $b \sqcup x = b \sqcup (a \sqcap b) \sqcup$ $\sqcup c = b \sqcup c$, that

(m2) $$c \leqslant a \rightarrow a \sqcap (b \sqcup c) = (a \sqcap b) \sqcup c.$$

The lattice axioms imply

$$c \leqslant a \rightarrow a \sqcap (b \sqcup c) \geqslant (a \sqcap b) \sqcup c,$$

so that for the proof of (m2) we have only to prove

(m2u) $$c \leqslant a \rightarrow a \sqcap (b \sqcup c) \leqslant (a \sqcap b) \sqcup c.$$

But (m2) again implies (m1); for if we add the assumption $a \sqcap b \leqslant c$ to those of (m2), then $(a \sqcap b) \sqcup c = c$.

If one interchanges $\leqslant$ with $\geqslant$ and $\sqcap$ with $\sqcup$ in (m2), then the dual law

(3) $$c \geqslant a \rightarrow a \sqcup (b \sqcap c) = (a \sqcup b) \sqcap c$$

is obtained. But this is a consequence of (m2) if the validity of (m2) is assumed for all a, b, c; one has only to interchange a and c. We say that *the modular law is self-dual.*

If in (3) one adds the assumption $c \leqslant a \sqcup b$, then $(a \sqcup b) \sqcap c = c$, and we obtain

$$a \leqslant c \leqslant a \sqcup b \rightarrow a \sqcup (b \sqcap c) = c$$

or, after changing the letters,

$$b \leqslant y \leqslant a \sqcup b \rightarrow b \sqcup (a \sqcap y) = y;$$

this is the dual statement to (m1), which is then a consequence of (m1).

The example ($\bar{m}$), which is used frequently, is typical in the following sense: *every non-modular lattice* ($V, \leqslant$) *contains a sub-lattice with the order diagram* ($\bar{m}$).

Proof. If V is not modular, then V contains elements a, b, c with

$$a \sqcap b \leqslant c \leqslant a \wedge a \sqcap (b \sqcup c) > c.$$

We set $a \sqcap (b \sqcup c) = a'$. Then it is easy to verify the relations

$$a \sqcap b \leqslant c < a' < b \sqcup c,$$

$$a \sqcap b \leqslant b \leqslant b \sqcup c \text{ (see Fig. 29).}$$

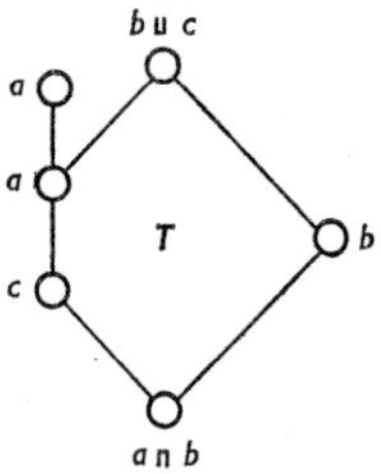

Fig. 29

$T = \{a \sqcap b, c, a', b \sqcup c, b\}$ forms a sub-lattice (this has to be checked, of course) with the order diagram ($\bar{m}$). But we still have to show that no two elements of T coincide. For this purpose a number of cases have to be checked. We consider only one of them: if $b = b \sqcup c$, then $a' = a \sqcap (b \sqcup c) = a \sqcap b \leqslant c$ in contradiction to $c < a'$.

Every modular lattice is strictly semi-modular in both directions. This follows from the fact that in a modular lattice the hypothesis in the definition of strict semi-modularity

$$a \sqcap b < c < a < c \sqcup b$$

can never be satisfied.

Proof. From $a \sqcap b < c < a$ it follows by (m1) that $a \sqcap (b \sqcup c) = c$.
From $a < c \sqcup b$ it follows that $a \sqcap (b \sqcup c) = a$.

Conversely, *one* semi-modularity does not imply modularity; this is shown by the examples of Fig. 30. 1 (lsm), and Fig. 30. 2 (usm).

Apparently even (lsm) and (usm) together do not imply modularity.

In Fig. 31 it follows from the order diagram for a, b, c, $a \sqcap b$, $c \sqcup b$ first of all that there exist s and t with $a \sqcap b < s < b$ and $b < t < c \sqcup b$.

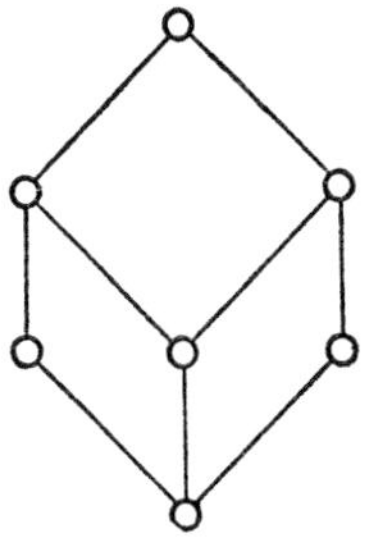

Fig. 30. 1 (lsm)

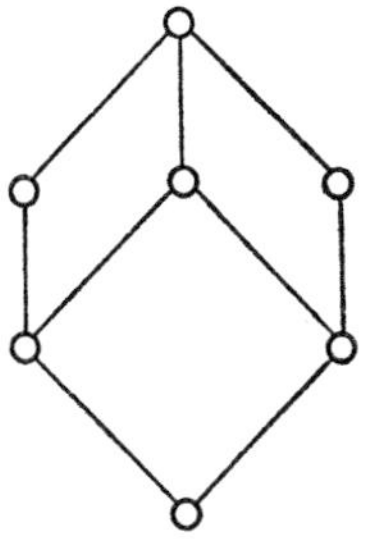

Fig. 30. 2 (usm)

Next, the existence of further elements in the sub-lattices $t/a \sqcap b$ and $c \sqcup b/s$ follows, etc. Probably there arises a semi-modular lattice in both directions that is not modular and not of finite length. However, it can be proved:

If $(V, \leqslant)$ *is of finite length below and if* (lsm) *and* (usm) *hold, then* $(V, \leqslant)$ *is modular.*

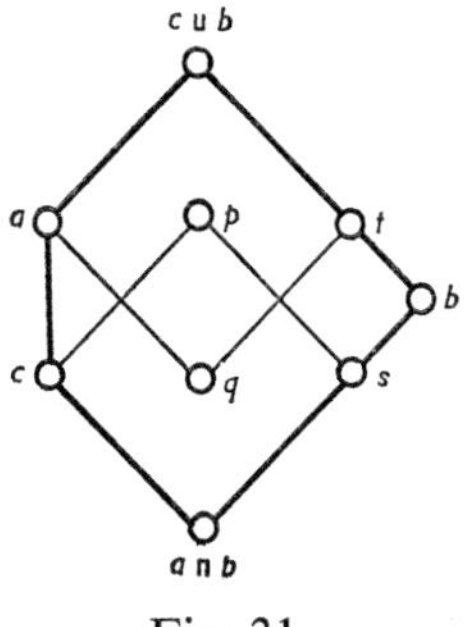

Fig. 31

Proof. As a consequence of the assumptions we have the dimension equation § 2, (4) or (5). We want to show that this implies (m1). Suppose, then, that $a \sqcap b \leqslant x \leqslant a$: then we have

$$a \sqcap (b \sqcup x) \geqslant x.$$

To prove that equality holds here we have only to show that

$$\delta(a \sqcap (b \sqcup x)) = \delta x.$$

Now we have

$$\begin{aligned}\delta(a \sqcap (b \sqcup x)) &= \delta a + \delta(b \sqcup x) - \delta(a \sqcup b \sqcup x)\\ &= \delta a + \delta b + \delta x - \delta(b \sqcap x) - \delta(a \sqcup b \sqcup x).\end{aligned}$$

From $a \sqcap b \leqslant x \leqslant a$ it follows that $b \sqcap x = a \sqcap b$ and $a \sqcup b \sqcup x = a \sqcup b$. So we obtain (with the help of the dimension equation)

$$\delta(a \sqcap (b \sqcup x)) = \delta a + \delta b + \delta x - \delta(a \sqcap b) - \delta(a \sqcup b) = \delta x.$$

The fact that, conversely, modularity and finite length below imply the dimension equation follows from the arguments at the beginning of this section; namely from the fact that $a \sqcup b/a$ can be mapped isomorphically onto $b/a \sqcap b$.

The isomorphism of the intervals $a \sqcup b/a$ and $b/a \sqcap b$ yields the following stronger form of the chain theorem:

Refinement theorem. In a modular lattice any two finite chains between the same elements

$$K_x\colon a = x_0 > x_1 > \ldots > x_l = b,$$
$$K_y\colon a = y_0 > y_1 > \ldots > y_m = b,$$

have isomorphic refinements.

Here two chains are called isomorphic if their intervals are isomorphic (apart from order).

It is not assumed that K_x, K_y are maximal chains, nor that the intervals x_i/x_{i+1}, y_k/y_{k+1} have finite length.

A generalization of this theorem will be proved in § 5.5, and so we omit a proof of the refinement theorem here.

§ 4. Normal subgroups of a group

Modular lattices arise at an important place in mathematics:

The normal subgroups of a group form a modular lattice relative to the order relation $\leqslant \leftrightharpoons \subseteq$.

We give a short account of the requisite concepts of group theory: let $(e, \cdot) = \mathfrak{G}$ be the given group. $a \subseteq e$ is called a subgroup if $(a, \cdot)$ is a group. For this it is necessary and sufficient that if $\alpha_1 \in a, \alpha_2 \in a$, then $\alpha_1 \cdot \alpha_2^{-1} \in a$.

A subgroup $a \subseteq e$ is called normal if

$$\alpha \in a \wedge \xi \in e \rightarrow \xi^{-1}\alpha\xi = \alpha' \in a,$$

in other words,

$$\bigwedge_{\alpha \in a} \bigwedge_{\xi \in e} \bigvee_{\alpha' \in a} \alpha\xi = \xi\alpha'.$$

If r and s are subsets of e, then the *product* $r \cdot s$, or simply rs, is defined as the set of all products $\varrho\sigma$, $\varrho \in r$, $\sigma \in s$.

$$rs = \{\varrho\sigma;\ \varrho \in r,\ \sigma \in s\}.$$

In general $rs \neq sr$. If r and s are subgroups (always of $(e, \cdot)$), then rs is a subgroup if and only if $rs = sr$.

Proof. We denote elements of r by $\varrho, \varrho_1, \varrho_2, \ldots$, elements of s by $\sigma, \sigma_1, \sigma_2, \ldots$ and similarly for other letters.

rs is a subgroup if and only if for any four elements $\varrho_1, \sigma_1, \varrho_2, \sigma_2$ we have

$$\varrho_1 \sigma_1 (\varrho_2 \sigma_2)^{-1} = \varrho_1 \sigma_1 \sigma_2^{-1} \varrho_2^{-1} = \varrho\sigma.$$

Since s is a subgroup, we have $\sigma_1 \sigma_2^{-1} = \sigma_3 \in s$. Our condition becomes

$$\varrho_1 \sigma_3 \varrho_2^{-1} = \varrho\sigma$$

or with

$$\varrho_1^{-1}\varrho = \varrho_3 \colon \quad \sigma_3 \varrho_2^{-1} = \varrho_3 \sigma.$$

This must hold for arbitrary σ_3, σ in s, ϱ_2, ϱ_3 in r.

A special case is:

If a is a normal subgroup and x an arbitrary subset of e, then

$$ax = xa.$$

For by the definition of a normal subgroup we have for all ξ in e: $\alpha\xi = \xi\alpha'$.

If a is a normal subgroup and x a subgroup, then ax is a subgroup.

On the other hand: every subgroup containing a and x also contains ax, so that in the lattice of subgroups $a \sqcup x = ax$, provided a is normal.

If a and b are normal, then ab is also normal, as is seen directly from the definition. Hence in the lattice of normal subgroups of $(e, \cdot)$ we always have $a \sqcup x = ax$.

It is even easier to determine $a \sqcap b$ in the lattice of normal subgroups for it is simply the set-theoretical intersection

$$a \sqcap b = a \cap b.$$

Now we shall show that the lattice of normal subgroups $(Ne, \subseteq)$ is modular. What we have to show is (see § 3):

(m1u) $\qquad a \sqcap b \subseteq c \subseteq a \rightarrow a \sqcap (b \sqcup c) \subseteq c.$

Suppose that

$$\xi \in a \sqcap (b \sqcup c) = a \cap (bc),$$

i.e. $$\xi = \alpha \in a \text{ and } \xi = \beta\gamma, \beta \in b, \gamma \in c.$$

Since $c \subseteq a$ we have $\gamma = \alpha' \in \alpha$, hence

$$\alpha = \beta\alpha',$$

i.e. also $$\beta \in a; \text{ hence } \beta \in a \cap b \subseteq c,$$

i.e. $$\xi = \beta\gamma \in c.$$

The proof can be extended to *groups with operators*. By an operator we mean an endomorphism, i.e. a mapping

$$\xi \nrightarrow \omega\xi \text{ with } \omega(\xi\eta) = \omega\xi \cdot \omega\eta.$$

If a set Ω of operators is given, a subgroup $a \subseteq e$ is called *admissible* relative to Ω if

$$\bigwedge_{\omega \in \Omega} \bigwedge_{\alpha \in a} \omega\alpha \in a.$$

The lattice of admissible normal subgroups of a group with operators is modular.

Among the groups with operators are the *vector spaces*. For the general theory we may refer to P. Halmos, 'Finite-dimensional Vector spaces', 2nd ed., Van Nostrand, New York–London 1958; D. T. Finkbeiner, 'Introduction to Matrices and Linear Transformations', Freeman & Company, San Francisco–London 1960.

We give a brief description of the vector space of dimension k over a field Ω (for example Ω can be the field of real numbers). The elements of e are the k-tuples of elements of Ω:

$$\mathfrak{x} = (\xi_1, \ldots, \xi_k), \quad \mathfrak{y} = (\eta_1, \ldots, \eta_k), \quad \xi_\kappa, \eta_\kappa \in \Omega.$$

An internal operation '+' is defined by

$$\mathfrak{x} + \mathfrak{y} = (\xi_1 + \eta_1, \ldots, \xi_k + \eta_k)$$

and an external operation '·' with the operator domain Ω by

$$\omega \cdot \mathfrak{x} = (\omega\xi_1, \ldots, \omega\xi_k), \quad \omega \in \Omega;$$

here $\omega\xi_\kappa$ is the product defined in the field Ω.

$(e, +)$ is then a commutative group, and every mapping $\mathfrak{x} \nrightarrow \omega \cdot \mathfrak{x}$ is an endomorphism of this group. The admissible subgroups are the subspaces; since the group is commutative, they are also the admissible normal subgroups. The lattice of these Ω-admissible normal subgroups is denoted by $(\mathfrak{L}e, \subseteq)$.

The dimension of a vector space is defined as the maximal number of linearly independent vectors. For the subspaces of our vector space e it coincides with the lattice-theoretical definition (length of a maximal chain starting from n). Here n is the subspace consisting of the null vector $\mathfrak{O}$ only.

Apart from n the subspaces can be interpreted as elements of a projective geometry: the subspaces

of dimension 1 as points,
2 as lines,
3 as planes, etc.,
$k-1$ as hyperplanes,
k as the projective space.

The geometric dimension is smaller by 1 than the lattice-theoretical. The k-tuples are homogeneous point coordinates.

§ 5. The algebra of relations

Since every normal subgroup of a group corresponds to a congruence relation, but in other structures not every congruence relation to a sub-formation, we may expect more general results when we transfer the ideas of the preceding section to congruence relations.

A congruence relation is (1) binary, (2) compatible with the defining relations of the formation in question, (3) an equivalence relation. Relations with the first and second property are called (following Lorenzen) *correspondences*.

5.1. Rules of calculation

We begin by considering *binary relations* $R, S, \ldots$ between the elements of a *single* set M. Such a relation is a subset of the product

$$R \subseteq M \times M.$$

$M \times M$ itself is also a binary relation, the 'all-relation' U, which holds between any two elements of M.

Since binary relations are regarded as subsets, set-theoretical inclusion is an order relation for them; we note the characteristic rules of calculation

(11) $R \subseteq R$ (Reflexivity)

(12) $E \subseteq S \wedge S \subseteq T \rightarrow R \subseteq T$ (Transitivity)

(13) $R \subseteq S \wedge S \subseteq R \rightarrow R = S$ (Anti-symmetry)

Furthermore $R \sqcap S = R \cap S$. This relation is characterized by

$$x(R \sqcap S)y \leftrightarrow xRy \wedge xSy$$

and can therefore be called *conjunction* and read as 'R and S'. It is characterized by

$$\text{(II)} \qquad R \subseteq S \wedge R \subseteq T \leftrightarrow R \subseteq S \sqcap T.$$

As was shown earlier,

$$S \sqcap T = T \sqcap S.$$

The intersection of arbitrarily many R_i, $i \in I$, can also be formed:

$$x(\bigsqcap_I R_i)y \leftrightarrow \bigwedge_{i \in I} xR_iy.$$

Thus, relations form a complete semi-lattice, which could be made into a complete lattice by the operation $R \cup S$ or $\bigcup_{i \in I} R_i$, respectively. But for reasons to be discussed later we do not consider this operation.

The relation defined by

$$xRSy \leftrightarrow \bigvee_z xRz \wedge zSy$$

is called the product of the relations R and S.

Examples (see also Chapter I, § 4.1).

1) If k and l are normal subgroups of a group g and

$$\xi K \zeta \leftrightharpoons \xi \equiv \zeta (\operatorname{mod} k), \text{ i.e. } \xi\zeta^{-1} = \kappa \in k,$$
$$\zeta L \eta \leftrightharpoons \zeta \equiv \eta (\operatorname{mod} l), \text{ i.e. } \zeta\eta^{-1} = \lambda \in l,$$

then

$$\xi KL\eta \leftrightarrow \bigvee_\zeta \xi\zeta^{-1} = \kappa \wedge \zeta\eta^{-1} = \lambda,$$

i.e.

$$\xi\eta^{-1} = \kappa\lambda.$$

But the elements $\kappa\lambda$ are precisely the elements of the product kl; so we obtain (the details are left to the reader)

$$\xi KL\eta \leftrightarrow \xi \equiv \eta (\operatorname{mod} kl).$$

2) If for integers x, y, z, h, k,

$$xRz \leftrightharpoons x \equiv z (\operatorname{mod} g), \text{ i.e. } x-z = kg,$$
$$zSy \leftrightharpoons z \equiv y (\operatorname{mod} h), \text{ i.e. } z-y = lh,$$

then $xRSy$ holds if and only if there is a z satisfying both equations, i.e. if

$$x-y = kg+lh.$$

Since all numbers of the form $kg+lh$ are multiples of the greatest common divisor (g,h), we obtain (the reader should supply the details)

$$xRSy \leftrightarrow x \equiv y\,(\mathrm{mod}\,(g,h)).$$

The product is *associative*:

(III, 1) $$R(ST) = (RS)T.$$

This can be verified immediately.

As a link between product and order relation we have

(III, 2) $$R_1 \subseteq S_1 \wedge R_2 \subseteq S_2 \rightarrow R_1R_2 \subseteq S_1S_2.$$

Proof.

$$xR_1R_2y \text{ means } \bigvee_z xR_1z \wedge zR_2y.$$

From $R_1 \subseteq S_1$ follows $xR_1z \rightarrow xS_1z$,
from $R_2 \subseteq S_2$ follows $zR_2y \rightarrow zS_2y$.

Therefore

$$xR_1R_2y \rightarrow \bigvee_z xS_1z \wedge zS_2y, \text{ i.e. } xS_1S_2y.$$

The relation of equality D: $xDy \leftrightharpoons x=y$ is the unit element of this multiplication of relations: for every relation R we have

(III, 3) $$DR = RD = R.$$

The relation R defined by

$$x\tilde{R}y \leftrightharpoons yRx$$

is called the *inverse relation* to R.

It is easy to see that

(IV, 1) $$\tilde{\tilde{R}} = R$$

(IV, 2) $$\widetilde{RS} = \tilde{S}\tilde{R}$$

(IV, 3) $$\widetilde{R \sqcap S} = \tilde{R} \sqcap \tilde{S}$$

(IV, 4) $$R \subseteq S \rightarrow \tilde{R} \subseteq \tilde{S}.$$

A connection between product and conjunction (intersection) is

(V) $$RS \sqcap T \subseteq (R \sqcap T\tilde{S})(S \sqcap \tilde{R}T).$$

Proof.

$$\begin{aligned} x(RS \sqcap T)y &\leftrightarrow \bigvee_z xRz \wedge zSy \wedge xTy \\ &\leftrightarrow \bigvee_z xRz \wedge xTy \wedge y\tilde{S}z \wedge zSy \wedge z\tilde{R}x \wedge xTy \\ &\rightarrow \bigvee_z x(R \sqcap T\tilde{S})z \wedge z(S \sqcap \tilde{R}T)y \\ &\leftrightarrow x(R \sqcap T\tilde{S})(S \sqcap \tilde{R}T)y. \end{aligned}$$

The transition from the second to the third line of the proof is not reversible; from $x(R \sqcap TS)z$ it follows that $\bigvee_w (xRz \wedge xTw \wedge wSz)$, but not that $w=y$.

A set of objects (here: binary relations) for which there are defined an order relation ($R \subseteq S$), two operations ($R \sqcap S$ and RS) and a mapping (R into R) satisfying the laws I–V is called a *bundle.*

5.2. Correspondences

The second property of a congruence relation we listed was compatibility with the defining operations of a formation.

Suppose that in the set M the operations

$$f_\kappa(x_1, \ldots, x_{n_\kappa}) = u_\kappa, \quad \kappa = 1, \ldots, k$$

are given. As an abbreviation we set

$$(x_1, \ldots, x_{n_\kappa}) = \mathfrak{x}, \quad (f_1, \ldots, f_k) = \Phi$$

and we denote the formation by (M, Φ).

A binary relation R is called *compatible* with the operation f (see Chapter IV, § 1.3) if

$$\bigwedge_\nu x_\nu R y_\nu \rightarrow f(\mathfrak{x}) R f(\mathfrak{y}).$$

If R is compatible with all f of Φ, then R is called a *correspondence* of the formation (M, Φ). The set of all correspondences of (M, Φ) is denoted by $\mathfrak{R}(M, \Phi)$ or for fixed (M, Φ) briefly by $\mathfrak{R}$.

Theorem. The correspondences of a formation form a bundle under the operations $\sim$, $\sqcap$, $\cdot$ defined in § 5.1.

What we have to prove is:

1) $D \in \mathfrak{R}$.—This is obviously the case.

2) From $R \in \mathfrak{R} \wedge S \in \mathfrak{R}$ it follows that

$$\text{a)}\ \tilde{R} \in \mathfrak{R},$$
$$\text{b)}\ R \sqcap S \in \mathfrak{R},$$
$$\text{c)}\ RS \in \mathfrak{R}.$$

The proofs are trivial as soon as one writes down the assumptions and the assertions. The assumptions are:

$$\bigwedge_{\nu} x_\nu R y_\nu \to f(\mathfrak{x}) R f(\mathfrak{y}),$$
$$\bigwedge_{\nu} x_\nu S y_\nu \to f(\mathfrak{x}) S f(\mathfrak{y}).$$

The assertions are:

a) $$\bigwedge_{\nu} x_\nu \tilde{R} y_\nu \to f(\mathfrak{x}) \tilde{R} f(\mathfrak{y}),$$

b) $$\bigwedge_{\nu} (x_\nu R y_\nu \wedge x_\nu S y_\nu) \to f(\mathfrak{x}) R f(\mathfrak{y}) \wedge f(\mathfrak{x}) S f(\mathfrak{y}),$$

c) $$\bigwedge_{\nu} \bigvee_{z\nu} (x_\nu R z_\nu \wedge z_\nu S y_\nu) \to \bigvee_{w} (f(\mathfrak{x}) R w \wedge w S f(\mathfrak{y})),$$

and $w = f(\mathfrak{z})$ satisfies the requirements.

3) The laws I–V are satisfied, because they hold for all binary relations on M.

5.3. *Equivalence relations*

Among the binary relations in a set M equivalences, which we denote by $A, B, C, \ldots$, can be characterized as follows:

(1) $$D \subseteq A, \text{ i.e. } x = y \to xAy \quad \text{(Reflexivity)},$$

(2) $$A\tilde{A} \subseteq A, \text{ i.e. } xAz \wedge z\tilde{A}y \to xAy,$$
$$\text{i.e. } xAz \wedge yAz \to xAy \quad \text{(Comparability)},$$

(on the basis of the bundle axioms alone, this implies symmetry)

(3) $$\tilde{A} = A.$$

Proof. $\tilde{A} = D\tilde{A} \subseteq A\tilde{A} \subseteq A$, hence $\tilde{A} \subseteq A$.

By (IV, 1) and (IV, 4) this implies $\tilde{\tilde{A}} = \tilde{A} \subseteq A$.

From (2) and (3) it follows that $AA \subseteq A$.

On the other hand, from (1) and (III, 2) it follows that

$$A = AD \subseteq AA,$$

hence

(4) $$AA = A\tilde{A} = A.$$

If A and B are equivalences, then so is $A \sqcap B$.

Proof. a) From $D \subseteq A$ and $D \subseteq B$ it follows that $D \subseteq A \sqcap B$.

b) We have to show: $(A \sqcap B)(\tilde{A} \sqcap B) \subseteq A \sqcap B$.

Now

$$A \sqcap B \subseteq A, \quad \tilde{A} \sqcap \tilde{B} \subseteq \tilde{A},$$

hence

$$(A \sqcap B)(\tilde{A} \sqcap \tilde{B}) \subseteq A\tilde{A} = A.$$

Similarly:

$$(A \sqcap B)(\tilde{A} \sqcap \tilde{B}) \subseteq B\tilde{B} = B.$$

So the result follows from (II).

If A and B are equivalences, then AB is an equivalence if and only if $AB = BA$.

Proof.

1) If AB is an equivalence, then by (3) $\tilde{A}B = AB$. On the other hand, by (IV, 1) and (3) $AB = BA = BA$.

2) Suppose that $\widetilde{AB} = \tilde{B}\tilde{A}$.

a) From $D \subseteq A$ and $D \subseteq B$ it follows that $D = DD \subseteq AB$.

b) $(AB)(\widetilde{AB}) = AB\tilde{B}\tilde{A} = AB\tilde{A} = BA\tilde{A} = BA = AB$.

Commutativity holds in algebraically important cases: if A and B are congruence relations of a group, then $AB = BA$.

We denote the elements of the group by small Greek letters. The assumption is:

$$\xi AB\eta, \text{ i.e. } \bigvee_{\zeta} \xi A\zeta \wedge \zeta B\eta;$$

the assertion is:

$$\xi BA\eta, \text{ i.e. } \bigvee_{\vartheta} \xi B\vartheta \wedge \vartheta A\eta.$$

To derive, first of all, from $\xi A\zeta$ a statement of the form $\ldots A\eta$ we multiply by $\zeta^{-1}\eta$. Since A is compatible with the group multiplication, we have

$$\xi\zeta^{-1}\eta A\eta.$$

It is easily verified that $\vartheta = \xi\zeta^{-1}$ satisfies the requirements: multiplication of $\zeta B\eta$ by $\xi\zeta^{-1}$ yields $\xi B\xi\zeta^{-1}\eta$.

A bundle in which for all R, S

$$RS = SR$$

is called *commutative*.

The congruence relations of a group form a commutative bundle. But then the same result holds for even richer structures. Without aiming at a general precise formulation we illustrate this in the example of a ring. A ring is a group under addition. The set $\mathfrak{R}_R$ of congruence relations of the ring is therefore a subset of the set $\mathfrak{R}_G$ of congruence relations of its additive group. If $\mathfrak{R}_G$ is commutative, then so is $\mathfrak{R}_R$.

5.3a. The lattice of equivalences

This paragraph is not required for the rest of § 5.

The congruences of a lattice do not, in general, satisfy $AB = BA$.

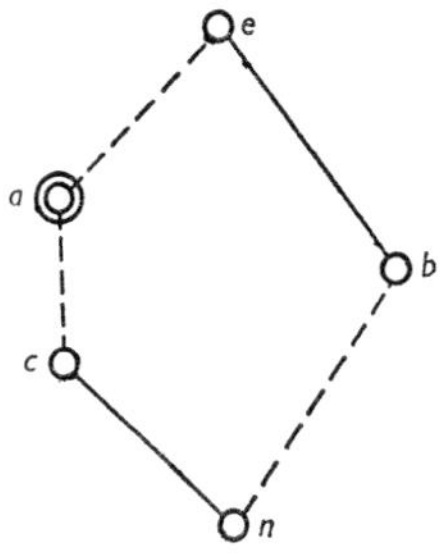

Fig. 32

Example. In the lattice $(\bar{m})$ let A be the equivalence with the equivalence classes $\{e,a,c\}$, $\{b,n\}$, B the equivalence with the classes $\{e,b\}$, $\{a\}$, $\{c,n\}$. In Fig. 32 A is characterized by broken lines, B by solid lines and the second circle around a. One can check by trying all possibilities that A and B are congruences. Now we have $aAc \wedge cBn$, hence $aABn$, whereas a stands in the relation B only to itself so that $aBAx$ holds only for those x that satisfy aAx, i.e. only for $x = a$, e, c.

Now we examine, $A \sqcup B = S$, the smallest equivalence containing A and B, in the first instance for the equivalences of a set.

From $A \subseteq S$ and $B \subseteq S$ it follows that $AB \subseteq S$ and then $ABA \subseteq SS = S$ etc. Therefore S contains all finite products P_i of A and B, hence also $Q = \bigcup P_i$.

Assertion: Q is an equivalence.

Proof. 1) $D \subseteq Q$, for $D \subseteq A$ and $A \subseteq Q$.

2) $QQ \subseteq Q$,

for xQz means: there is a P_i such that xP_iz;

zQy means: there is a P_k such that $x\tilde{P}_ky$.

If $xQ\tilde{Q}y$ holds, then there exist P_i, P_k such that $xP_i\tilde{P}_ky$ holds. But since $\tilde{A}=A$, $\tilde{B}=B$, $P_i\tilde{P}_k$ is again a finite product of A, B, i.e. xQy holds.

Therefore in the set of equivalences of a set we have $A \sqcup B=Q$. Q is called the *transitive hull* of AB.

If A and B are *correspondences of a formation*, then all finite products are also correspondences (see § 5.2). The fact that then $Q=\bigcup P_i$ is also a correspondence will be shown for a binary operation $\top$:

Assertion: $aQb \wedge cQd \rightarrow (a \top c)Q(b \top d)$.

Proof. aQb means: there is a P_i with aP_ib,

cQd means: there is a P_k with cP_kd.

But since bP_kb and cP_ic hold, so do aP_iP_kb and cP_iP_kd. Now P_iP_k is a finite product of A and B and therefore a correspondence. The assertion follows from this.

If A and B are simultaneously equivalences and correspondences, hence congruences, then the finite products are not always congruences, but $\bigcup P_i$ is. Also in the set $\mathfrak{K}(\mathfrak{M})$ of congruences of a formation $\mathfrak{M}$ we have $A \sqcup B=\bigcup P_i$. With this $\sqcup$ and $\sqcap=\cap$, $\mathfrak{K}(\mathfrak{M})$ forms a lattice $(\mathfrak{K}(\mathfrak{M}),\sqcap,\sqcup)$.

We show: *The lattice of congruences of a lattice* $\mathfrak{M}=(V,\sqcap,\sqcup)$ *is distributive.*

The symbols $\sqcap$, $\sqcup$ now occur with different meanings: between small Latin letters they mean the operations on elements of V, between capital Latin letters they mean the operations with congruences over the lattice V whose definitions we now repeat:

$$x(B \sqcap C)y \leftrightharpoons xBy \wedge xCy.$$

$x(B \sqcup C)y$ means: there is a finite product $R_1R_2\ldots R_k$, in which every R_κ is equal to B or to C such that $xR_1R_2\ldots R_ky$ holds, in other words, that there exist elements z_0, $z_1,\ldots,z_k$ in V for which $x=z_0$, $z_{\kappa-1}R_\kappa z_\kappa$, $z_k=y$ hold.

We claim (see Chapter VI, § 1.1, (D1u)):

$$A \sqcap (B \sqcup C) \subseteq (A \sqcap B) \sqcup (A \sqcap C),$$

i.e.

$$x[A \sqcap (B \sqcup C)]y \rightarrow x[(A \sqcap B) \sqcup (A \sqcap C)]y.$$

Proof. The assumption is: xAy holds and there exist $z_0, \ldots, z_k$ with $x = z_0$, $z_{\kappa-1} R_\kappa z_\kappa$ (for all $\kappa = 1, \ldots, k$) $z_k = y$; $R_\kappa = B$ or C.

If we now set

$$w_\kappa = [(x \sqcap y) \sqcup z_\kappa] \sqcap (x \sqcup y),$$

then it is easy to see that

$$x = w_0, w_{\kappa-1} R_\kappa w_\kappa \text{ (for } \kappa = 1, \ldots, k), \; w_k = y.$$

Moreover, as we shall prove below, $w_{\kappa-1} A w_\kappa$; i.e. the sequence $w_0, \ldots, w_k$ has the property

$$w_0 = x, w_{\kappa-1} (A \sqcap R_\kappa) w_\kappa, w_k = y,$$

and this means that $x[(A \sqcap b) \sqcup (A \sqcap C)]y$, as required.

Proof of $w_{\kappa-1} A w_\kappa$ for all $\kappa = 1, \ldots, k$.

Obviously $x \sqcap y \leqslant w_\kappa \leqslant x \sqcup y$. And now the result follows from the *Lemma*:

If xAy and $x \sqcap y \leqslant {}^u_v \leqslant x \sqcup y$ holds, then so does uAv.

Proof. Under the assumptions stated we have (yAx and)

$$u = u \sqcup (x \sqcap y) A u \sqcup (x \sqcap x) = u \sqcup x$$
$$u = u \sqcap (x \sqcup y) A u \sqcap (x \sqcup x) = u \sqcap x$$
$$x = x \sqcap (x \sqcup u) A x \sqcap u A u, \text{ i.e. } xAu.$$

Similarly one proves vAy. This implies uAv.

5.4. Applications to groups

In a normal series of a group $(e, \cdot)$

$$a_0 \subset a_1 \subset \ldots \subset a$$

every a_ν is normal in the successor $a_{\nu+1}$, but not always normal in the group; hence to the a_ν there correspond not always congruences but, as they are subgroups of e, equivalences that need not be compatible with the group multiplication and whose product is not always an equivalence. We have to consider this situation in more detail.

If $(e, \cdot)$ is a *group*, then with every subset $r \subseteq e$ we can associate a relation R as follows:

$$\xi R \eta \iff \xi \eta^{-1} \in r.$$

These relations are not always compatible with the group structure:

From

$$\xi_1 R \eta_1, \text{ i.e. } \xi_1 \eta_1^{-1} \in r$$

and

$$\xi_2 R \eta_2, \text{ i.e. } \xi_2 \eta_2^{-1} \in r$$

it does not always follow that

$$\xi_1 \xi_2 R \eta_1 \eta_2, \text{ i.e. } \xi_1 \xi_2 \eta_2^{-1} \eta_1^{-1} \in r.$$

As we know, this holds only when r is a normal subgroup of e.

On the other hand, naturally one does not obtain all binary relations on e in this way as images of subsets. For example, our relations have the property

$$\text{for all } \lambda \in e\colon \xi R \eta \;\rightarrow\; \xi \lambda R \eta \lambda.$$

Since subsets of groups are occasionally called complexes, we shall call the relations in question *complex relations*.

In order to apply the rules I–V we have to show that the converse of a complex relation and the conjunction and product of two complex relations R and S are again complex relations.

1) If $\xi R \eta$ means that $\xi \eta^{-1} \in r$,
then $\xi \tilde{R} \eta$ means $\eta R \xi$, i.e. $\eta \xi^{-1} = \varrho \in r$,
but then we have $\xi \eta^{-1} = \varrho^{-1}$. Again a subset is associated with R, namely $\tilde{r} = \{\varrho^{-1}; \varrho \in r\}$.

2) $\xi(R \sqcap S)\eta$ means that $\xi R \eta \wedge \xi S \eta$, i.e. $\xi \eta^{-1} \in r \wedge \xi \eta^{-1} \in s$, therefore $\xi(R \sqcap S)\eta$ holds if and only if $\xi \eta^{-1} \in r \cap s$. Therefore, $r \cap s$ is the subset associated with $R \sqcap S$.

3) If $\xi R S \eta$ holds, i.e. if there exists a ζ with

$$\xi R \zeta \wedge \zeta S \eta,$$

i.e.

$$\xi \zeta^{-1} = \varrho \in r, \quad \zeta \eta^{-1} = \sigma \in s,$$

then $\xi \eta^{-1} = \varrho \sigma$.

The set $rs \leftrightharpoons \{\varrho\sigma; \varrho \in r, \sigma \in s\}$ is precisely the product (see p. 85).

Conversely, if $\xi \eta^{-1} = \varrho \sigma$, then ζ can be determined from $\xi \zeta^{-1} = \varrho$: $\varrho^{-1} \xi = \zeta$. Then we have

$$\zeta \eta^{-1} = \varrho^{-1} \xi \eta^{-1} = \varrho^{-1} \varrho \sigma = \sigma.$$

The product rs corresponds to the relation RS.

Thus, the set of complex relations is closed under conjunction and product, and taking the inverse of a relation, and therefore forms a bundle.

The set $d=\{\epsilon\}$ where ϵ is the neutral element of the group is associated with the relation D; for $\xi D\eta \leftrightarrow \xi=\eta \leftrightarrow \xi\eta^{-1}=\epsilon$.

Note. Instead of associating subsets with relations, we could simply have defined for subsets of e:

$$r \subseteq s \text{ as inclusion}$$
$$r \cap s \text{ as intersection}$$
$$\tilde{r} = \{\varrho^{-1};\ \varrho \in r\},$$
$$rs = \{\varrho\sigma;\ \varrho \in r,\ \sigma \in s\}.$$

Then we would have to check the validity of rules I–V. For most of these rules this is very simple. For V the proof runs as follows:

The assumption is $\xi \in rs \cap t$,

the assertion is $\xi \in (r \cap t\tilde{s})(s \cap \tilde{r}t)$.

The assumption means that $\xi \in rs$, i.e. $\xi=\varrho\sigma(\varrho \in r,\ \sigma \in s)$

and at the same time $\xi = \tau(\tau \in t)$,

hence $\varrho\sigma = \tau$.

From this it follows that $\varrho=\tau\sigma^{-1}$, $\sigma=\varrho^{-1}\tau$.

Thus ξ is the product of $\varrho=\tau\sigma^{-1}$, which is an element of $r \cap t\tilde{s}$, and $\sigma=\varrho^{-1}\tau$, which is an element of $s \cap \tilde{r}t$.

A subset r is subgroup if $\epsilon \in r$, i.e. $d \subseteq r$, and if together with $\varrho_1 \in r$, $\varrho_2 \in r$ we have also $\varrho_1\varrho_2^{-1} \in r$, i.e. if $r\tilde{r} \subseteq r$.

For the associated relation R this means, of course,

$$D \subseteq R \text{ and } R\tilde{R} \subseteq R.$$

The subgroups therefore correspond precisely to the equivalence relations. But these, too, are not, in general, compatible with the group multiplication, and so are neither correspondences nor congruence relations.

If a, b are subsets of e, then b is a normal subgroup of a if $a \subseteq b$ and for every $\alpha \in a$ and $\beta \in b$ we have

$$\alpha^{-1}\beta\alpha \in b,$$

i.e. if for every subset r of a we have

$$rb = br.$$

5.5. The refinement theorem

The position we have arrived at can be described in general terms as follows: we are given a bundle whose elements are denoted by R, S, T,..., and in it a subset of equivalences for which we shall use the letters A, B, C,...; the rules of operation are I–V and, in addition, § 5.3, 1–4 for the equivalences. We define: an equivalence B is called *normal* relative to the equivalence A, if

$$\bigwedge_R R \subseteq A \rightarrow RB = BR.$$

If one now calls a chain of equivalences

$$A_0 \subseteq A_1 \subseteq \ldots \subseteq A_l$$

normal if A_i is normal relative to A_{i+1}, then we have the *refinement theorem: two normal chains $A_0 \subseteq A_1 \subseteq \ldots \subseteq A_l$ and $B_0 \subseteq B_1 \subseteq \ldots \subseteq B_m$ with equal ends $A_0 = B_0$, $A_l = B_m$ have projective refinements.* This is the generalization announced at the end of § 3. A pair B_1, B_2 is said to be *perspective* to A_1, A_2 from below if (see Fig. 33)

$$A_1 = A_2 B_1; \quad B_2 = A_2 \sqcap B_1.$$

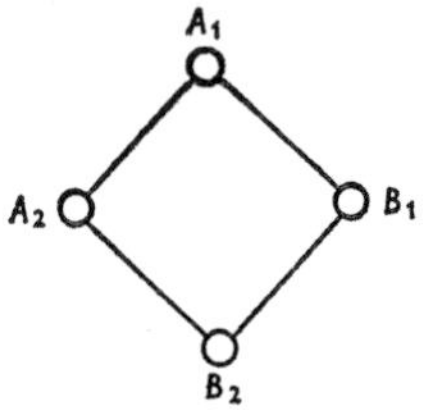

Fig. 33

Two pairs are said to be *projective* from below if there exists a pair that is perspective to both from below.

A projective refinement is found by inserting between A_{i-1} and A the element $A_{ik} = A_{i-1}(A_i \sqcap B_k)$ and between B_{k-1} and B_k the elements $B_{ki} = (A_i \sqcap B_k)B_{k-1}$. The fact that

$$A_{i-1} \subseteq A_{ik} \subseteq A_i, \; B_{k-1} \subseteq B_{ki} \subseteq B_k$$

is seen immediately.

If the relevant elements were commutative, then we would have $AB = A \sqcup B$, and the modular law (provided it holds, as for example in congruence relations for groups) would yield the necessary transformations. But now we have only (V), page 89, at our disposal.

If we assume here that $T=A$ is an equivalence and that $R\subseteq A$, then we obtain (stating the second assumption explicitly again)

(1a) $$R \subseteq A \;\rightarrow\; A \sqcap RS = R(A \sqcap S)$$

(1b) $$R \subseteq A \;\rightarrow\; A \sqcap SR = (A \sqcap S)R.$$

Proof of (1a). By (V) we have $A \sqcap RS \subseteq (A\tilde{S} \sqcap R)(\tilde{R}A \sqcap S)$.

Now $$A\tilde{S} \sqcap R \subseteq R,$$

$$\tilde{R}A \subseteq A, \text{ hence } \tilde{R}A \sqcap S \subseteq A \sqcap S,$$

hence $$A \sqcap RS \subseteq R(A \sqcap S).$$

On the other hand, $R\subseteq A$ and $A \sqcap S \leqslant A$,

hence $$R(A \sqcap S) \subseteq AA = A,$$

moreover $R \subseteq R$, $A \sqcap S \leqslant S$, hence $R(A \sqcap S) \subseteq RS$,

hence $$R(A \sqcap S) \subseteq A \sqcap RS.$$

Similarly one proves (1b).

If all the relevant relations are permutable equivalence relations, then (1a) and (1b) coincide and yield precisely the modular law.

In our case we obtain for A_{ik}, B_{ik} the representations

$$A_{ik} = A_{i-1}(A_i \sqcap B_k) = A_i \sqcap A_{i-1}B_k$$
$$B_{ki} = (A_i \sqcap B_k)B_{k-1} = B_k \sqcap A_iB_{k-1}.$$

In order to prove that the pair $A_{i,k}$; $A_{i,k-1}$ and $B_{k,i}$; $B_{k,i-1}$ are perspective, we form $P=A_{i,k} \sqcap B_{k,i}$ and $Q=A_{i,k-1} \sqcap B_{k,i-1}$ and show that $A_{i,k-1}\,P=A_{ik}$: $A_{i,k-1} \sqcap P=Q$. (See Fig. 34.)

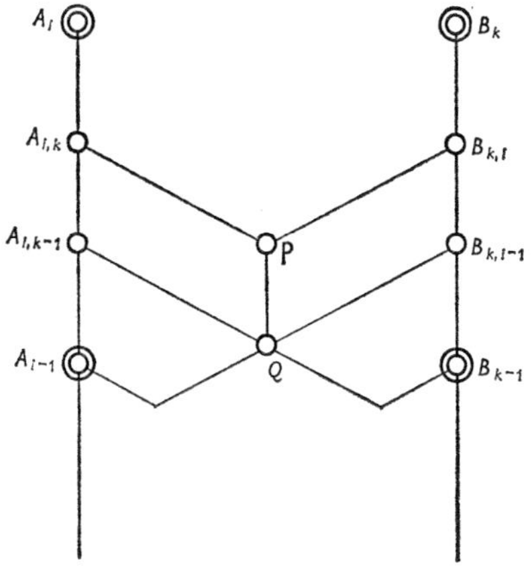

Fig. 34

Proof.

1) We have $P = A_i \sqcap A_{i-1}B_k \sqcap B_k \sqcap A_iB_{k-1} = A_i \sqcap B_k$, because $A_i \subseteq A_iB_{k-1}$ and $B_k \subseteq A_{i-1}B_k$.

Hence we have $A_{i,k-1}P = A_{i-1}(A_i \sqcap B_{k-1})(A_i \sqcap B_k)$.

But now $A_i \sqcap B_{k-1} \subseteq A_i \sqcap B_k$, and for two equivalences A and B we have

$$A \subseteq B \rightarrow AB \subseteq BB = B, \text{ on the other hand } B \subseteq AB.$$

Hence we have $A_{i,k-1}P = A_{i-1}(A_i \sqcap B_k) = A_{ik}$.

2) We have

$$Q = A_i \sqcap A_{i-1}B_{k-1} \sqcap B_k \sqcap A_{i-1}B_{k-1} = A_i \sqcap B_k \sqcap A_{i-1}B_{k-1}.$$

$$A_{i,k-1} \sqcap P = A_i \sqcap A_{i-1}B_{k-1} \sqcap A_i \sqcap B_k = Q.$$

The fact that P, Q is perspective to $B_{k,i}$, $B_{k,k-1}$ is proved correspondingly.

Finally it has to be shown that $A_{i,k-1} = A_{i-1}(A_i \sqcap B_{k-1})$ is normal relative to

$$A_{ik} = A_{i-1}(A_i \sqcap B_k).$$

This is a consequence of the following theorems:

(*i*) If $B \subseteq A$ and B is normal relative to A, then $B \sqcap C$ is normal relative to $A \sqcap C$.

> *Proof.* From $R \subseteq A \sqcap C$ follows $R \subseteq A$, hence $RB = BR$. Further, $R \subseteq C$, hence by (1a) and (1b) $R(B \sqcap C) = RB \sqcap C = BR \sqcap C = (B \sqcap C)R$. From this follows: $A_i \sqcap B_{i-1}$ is normal relative to $A_i \sqcap B_k$.

(*ii*) If $B \subseteq A$ and B and C are normal relative to A, then CB is normal to CA.

With $B = A_i \sqcap B_{k-1}$, $A = A_i \sqcap B_k$, $C = A_{i-1}$ the assumptions are satisfied. (Since A_{i-1} is normal relative to A_i, it is normal to $A_i \sqcap B_k$, as follows immediately from the definition.) With the proof of (*ii*) the original assertion is proved.

Proof of (*ii*).

1) From (V) it follows (if A is an equivalence) that

$$RA \sqcap SA \subseteq (RA\tilde{A} \sqcap S)(\tilde{S}RA \sqcap A).$$

Since A is an equivalence, we have $A\tilde{A} = A$, hence $RA\tilde{A} \sqcap S = RA \sqcap S$. Further, $\tilde{S}RA \sqcap A \subseteq A$, hence

$$RA \sqcap SA \subseteq (RA \sqcap S)A.$$

On the other hand $RA \sqcap S \subseteq RA$, hence $(RA \sqcap S)A \subseteq RAA = RA$

and
$$(RA \sqcap S)A \subseteq SA,$$

and so we have $(RA \sqcap S)A \subseteq RA \sqcap SA$, whence

(2a)
$$RA \sqcap SA = (RA \sqcap S)A.$$

In the same way one proves

(2b)
$$AR \sqcap AS = A(AR \sqcap S).$$

2) If C is normal relative to A, then C is normal to CA. The assumption states:

$$R \subseteq A \rightarrow RC = CR,$$

in particular,

$$AC = CA.$$

The assertion is

$$R \subseteq CA \rightarrow RC = CR.$$

Let $R \subseteq CA$; then $CR \subseteq CCA = CA$, hence

$$CR = CR \sqcap CA.$$

By (2b)

$$\begin{aligned} CR = CR \sqcap CA &= C(CR \sqcap A) \\ &= CC(CR \sqcap A), \text{ because } CC = C \\ &= C(CR \sqcap A)C \text{ by assumption,} \\ &\qquad \text{because } CR \sqcap A \subseteq A \\ &= CRC \text{ by the first line of this calculation.} \end{aligned}$$

In the same way one proves $RC = CRC$.

3) The assumptions of (*ii*) are:

Ass. 1. B normal relative to A, hence $R \subseteq A \rightarrow RB = BR$,

Ass. 2. C normal relative to A, hence $R \subseteq A \rightarrow RC = CR$,

Ass. 3. $B \subseteq A$.

The assertion is: CB is normal relative to CA, i.e.

$$R \subseteq CA \rightarrow RCB = CBR.$$

Let $R \subseteq CA$.

Then $RC \subseteq CAC = ACC = AC$, hence

(*) $\quad RC = RC \sqcap AC = (RC \sqcap A)C$ by (2a)

$$\begin{aligned} RCB &= (RC \sqcap A)CB \text{ by Ass. 2 and 3} \\ &= (RC \sqcap A)BC \\ &= B(RC \sqcap A)C \text{ by Ass. 1, because } RC \sqcap A \subseteq A \\ &= BRC \text{ by (*).} \end{aligned}$$

From $R \subseteq CA$, Ass. 2 and what has been proved under 2) it follows that

$$RC = CR.$$

Thus we have

$$RCB = BRC,$$

and from $BC = C$ the assertion follows.

On this point see P. Lorenzen, 'Über die Korrespondenzen einer Struktur', *Math. Z.* **60** (1954), 61–65.

§ 6. Complemented modular lattices

6.1. *The complement*

Example. In a vector space e of dimension k over a field Ω (see § 4, page 86) any k linearly independent vectors $\mathfrak{e}_1, \ldots, \mathfrak{e}_k$ form a basis, i.e. every vector $\mathfrak{x}$ of e can be represented uniquely in the form

$$\mathfrak{x} = \mathfrak{e}_1\xi_1 + \ldots + \mathfrak{e}_k\xi_k,\ \xi_k \in \Omega.$$

Every basis $\mathfrak{a}_1, \ldots, \mathfrak{a}_r$ of a subspace a of e can be extended to a basis $(\mathfrak{a}_1, \ldots, \mathfrak{a}_r, \mathfrak{a}_{r+1}, \ldots, \mathfrak{a}_k)$ of e. Then the subspace b spanned by $\mathfrak{a}_{r+1}, \ldots, \mathfrak{a}_k$ has the property

(1) $$a \sqcup b = e, \quad a \sqcap b = n.$$

Here n is the subspace consisting of the null-vector $\mathfrak{o}$ only. ($a \sqcup b$ denotes, of course, the smallest subspace of e containing a and b, $a \sqcap b$ the largest subspace contained in a and b.)

Definitions. In a lattice V with null-element n and unit element e an element b is called a *complement* to a if (1) holds. If V contains for every element at least one complement, then V is called *complemented.*

In a lattice that need not contain n or e an element b is called a *relative complement* to a in the interval v/d if $d \leqslant a \leqslant v$, $d \leqslant b \leqslant v$ and $a \sqcap b = d$, $a \sqcup b = v$. If every interval in V is complemented,[1] then V is called *relatively complemented.*

[1] Every interval v/d is a sub-lattice with the null-element d and the unit element v.

If V contains a null-element n and if all segments, i.e. the intervals a/n, are complemented, then V is called *segmentwise complemented.* A relatively complemented lattice is, of course, complemented if and only if it contains n and e. The fact that a complemented lattice need not be relatively complemented, nor even segmentwise complemented, is shown by the example $(\bar{m})$, Fig. 22.1, page 76. The elements a and c are complements to b—but in the interval a/n c has no relative complement.)

The example of a non-modular lattice is typical in the following sense: If a lattice is complemented and modular, then it is relatively complemented.

Proof. Let $d \leqslant a \leqslant v$. In the interval v/d we look for a relative complement b to a.

By assumption there exists an element c with

$$a \sqcap c = n, \quad a \sqcup c = e.$$

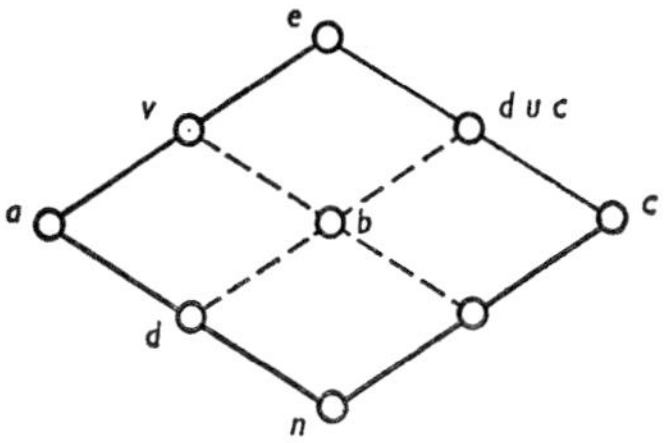

Fig. 35

Fig. 35 suggests that we try $b = v \sqcap (d \sqcup c)$. Then we have

$a \sqcap b = a \sqcap (d \sqcup c)$, because $a \leqslant v$
$= (a \sqcap c) \sqcup d$ by the modular law, because $d \leqslant a$
$= d$, because $a \sqcap c = n$.

$a \sqcup b = a \sqcup (v \sqcap (d \sqcup c)) = v \sqcap (d \sqcup c \sqcup a)$ by the modular law, because $a \leqslant v$,

$= v$, because $c \sqcup a = e$.

The lattice $(\mathfrak{L}e, \subseteq)$ of the subspaces of a vector space e is modular and complemented, and so relatively complemented.

6.2. Projective geometry

6.2.1. Introduction. The subspaces of a vector space e form on the one hand a projective geometry, on the other hand a complemented modular lattice of finite length. Now one can ask whether *every* complemented modular lattice V of finite length determines a projective geometry, or whether one can find for V a vector space e such that V is isomorphic to $\mathfrak{L}e$. This question has been treated, for example, by Baer[1] and in another way by Hermes.[2] We give here a partial sketch of a method, which is a slight modification of the way followed by Hermes and which emphasizes the point of view of relation theory.

There are two fundamental interpretations of geometry: either one regards points, lines, planes as objects of different kinds between which relations such as incidence are defined; this is the classical point of view which, among others, Euclid and Hilbert adopted. Or one starts out from the set of points and defines straight lines, planes, etc. as subsets of this set. Possibly the first interpretation is to be preferred for fundamental reasons. Nevertheless here we choose the second.

6.2.2. Relation-theoretical characterization. Let p be a set whose elements we call points and denote by small Greek letters. Suppose that in p a ternary relation A is defined satisfying the following axioms:

(r) Reflexivity: $\alpha = \beta \rightarrow A(\alpha, \beta, \gamma)$,

or written differently:[3]

$$\bigwedge_{\alpha}\bigwedge_{\gamma} A(\alpha, \alpha, \gamma).$$

(s) Symmetry:[4]

$$A(\alpha, \beta, \gamma) \rightarrow A(\beta, \gamma, \alpha) \rightarrow A(\alpha, \gamma, \beta)$$

(t) Transitivity:

$$\alpha \neq \beta \wedge A(\alpha, \beta, \gamma) \wedge A(\alpha, \beta, \delta) \rightarrow A(\alpha, \gamma, \delta).$$

Note. On account of (s) it then follows that

$$A(\beta, \gamma, \delta).$$

We read $A(\alpha, \beta, \gamma)$ as 'α, β, γ are linearly dependent (or collinear)' or 'γ is linearly dependent on α, β'. On account of symmetry it is

[1] R. Baer, 'Linear Algebra and Projective Geometry', New York 1952; in particular, Chapter VII.

[2] H. Hermes, 'Einführung in die Verbandstheorie' (see Bibliography), Chapter III, § 14–16.

[3] Here we do not write down the obvious $\bigwedge$-quantifiers.

[4] For a generalization of the concepts *reflexive* and *symmetric* see G. Pickert, 'Bemerkungen über Galois-Verbindungen', *Archiv d. Math.* **3** (1952), 285–289.

immaterial which of the points is regarded as linearly dependent on the others.

A can be regarded as a ternary analogue of an equivalence relation. An equivalence relation R partitions a set into equivalence classes: we define $K\alpha = \{\xi; \xi R\alpha\}$. Every element of the original set determines precisely one equivalence class; two classes have either no element or all elements in common. Similarly we now start out from pairs of elements and for $\alpha \neq \beta$ we form the set

$$l_2(\alpha, \beta) \leftrightharpoons \{\xi; A(\alpha, \beta, \xi)\}$$

and call it the *line* $\alpha\beta$.

Theorem 1a. Any two distinct points determine precisely one line (by definition).

Theorem 1b. If two lines have two points in common, they have all points in common.

Assumptions.

$$A(\alpha, \beta, \xi),\ A(\alpha, \beta, \eta),\ \alpha \neq \beta,\ \xi \neq \eta;$$
$$A(\gamma, \delta, \xi),\ A(\gamma, \delta, \eta),\ \gamma \neq \delta;$$
$$A(\alpha, \beta, \zeta).$$

Assertion.

$$A(\gamma, \delta, \zeta).$$

Proof. For $\zeta = \xi$ or $\zeta = \eta$ the assertion is true. Therefore we assume that $\zeta \neq \xi$, $\zeta \neq \eta$.

To begin with we use only the assumptions

$$A(\alpha, \beta, \xi),\ A(\alpha, \beta, \eta),\ A(\alpha, \beta, \zeta).$$

By symmetry and transitivity this implies

$$A(\alpha, \xi, \eta),\ A(\alpha, \xi, \zeta),\ A(\alpha, \eta, \zeta)$$

and this in turn implies $A(\xi, \eta, \zeta)$, namely when $\xi = \alpha$, because of the third, and when $\xi \neq \alpha$, because of the first two of these relations. So we have as an intermediate result:

Theorem 1c. Any three points of a line are linearly dependent.

Continuation of the proof of Theorem 1b:

$$\gamma \neq \delta \wedge A(\gamma, \delta, \xi) \wedge A(\gamma, \delta, \eta) \quad \rightarrow A(\gamma, \xi, \eta) \wedge A(\delta, \xi, \eta).$$
$$A(\gamma, \xi, \eta) \wedge A(\delta, \xi, \eta) \wedge A(\zeta, \xi, \eta) \rightarrow A(\gamma, \delta, \zeta) \text{ by Theorem 1c.}$$

In order to define *planes* we form a quaternary relation, a kind of relation product of A with itself:

$$\textit{Definition.}\ A_4(\alpha,\beta,\gamma,\delta) \Leftrightarrow \bigvee_{\eta} (A(\alpha,\beta,\eta) \wedge A(\eta,\gamma,\delta)).$$

When this relation holds we say that the four points α, β, γ, δ are *linearly dependent* and when $\neg\, A(\alpha,\beta,\gamma)$ we call the set

$$l_3(\alpha,\beta,\gamma) \Leftrightarrow \{\xi;\ A(\alpha,\beta,\gamma,\xi)\}$$

the *plane* $\alpha\beta\gamma$.

The definition amounts to this: ξ lies in the plane $\alpha\beta\gamma$ if the lines $\alpha\beta$ and $\gamma\xi$ have a point of intersection, in other words, the plane $\alpha\beta\gamma$ consists of the points of all lines that join γ to the points of $\alpha\beta$.

Now our task is to prove *reflexivity, symmetry,* and *transitivity* for the relation A_4.

1) *Reflexivity.* We have $A(\alpha,\beta,\gamma) \rightarrow A_4(\alpha,\beta,\gamma,\delta)$, for the definition is satisfied with $\eta=\gamma$.

2) *Symmetry.* From the definition of A_4 and the symmetry of A it follows that α can be permuted with β or γ with δ or both or α, β with γ, δ. There remains the question whether

$$A_4(\alpha,\beta,\gamma,\delta) \rightarrow A_4\,(\alpha,\gamma,\beta,\delta),$$

i.e. whether the statement

$$(q) \qquad \bigvee_{\eta} (A(\alpha,\beta,\eta) \wedge A(\eta,\gamma,\delta)) \rightarrow \bigvee_{\zeta} (A(\alpha,\gamma,\zeta) \wedge A(\zeta,\beta,\delta))$$

holds (Fig. 36). This statement does not follow from the preceding axioms. For if one interprets p as the Euclidiean plane and $A(\alpha,\beta,\gamma)$ as the statement that the points α, β, γ lie on a line, then (r), (s), (t) hold, but not always (q), for example when the lines $\alpha\gamma$ and $\beta\delta$ are parallel. *We adjoin* (q) *as a further axiom* (and so exclude Euclidean geometry as a possible interpretation of the axioms).

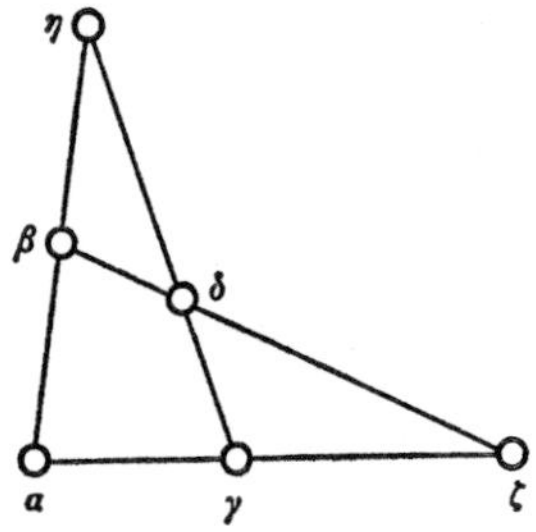

Fig. 36

That such an axiom is needed is plausible, because none of the preceding axioms guarantee the existence of any point. For this purpose even axioms of a different kind are required that postulate the existence, say, of at least four linearly independent points; they will not be discussed here. Axiom (q) is in a certain sense an analogue of Euclid's parallel postulate, because this too postulates the existence of a point of intersection of two lines under suitable conditions. It states: 'When a straight line meets two straight lines and makes the interior angles on the same side less than two right angles, then the two straight lines extended indefinitely meet on that side on which the angles are less than two right angles.'

3) The *transitivity* of A_4 has to be stated as follows:

$$\neg A(\alpha,\beta,\gamma) \wedge A_4(\alpha,\beta,\gamma,\varrho) \wedge A_4(\alpha,\beta,\gamma,\sigma) \rightarrow A_4(\alpha,\beta,\varrho,\sigma).$$

The assumptions are:

$$\neg A(\alpha,\beta,\gamma),$$

$$\bigvee_{\eta} (A(\alpha,\beta,\eta) \wedge A(\eta,\gamma,\varrho)),$$

$$\bigvee_{\zeta} (A(\alpha,\beta,\zeta) \wedge A(\zeta,\gamma,\sigma)).$$

The assertion is:

$$\bigvee_{\vartheta} (A(\alpha,\beta,\vartheta) \wedge A(\vartheta,\varrho,\sigma)).$$

Proof (see Fig. 37). Since the lines $\varrho\eta$ and $\sigma\zeta$ have the point γ in common, $\varrho\sigma$ and $\zeta\eta$ have, by (q), a point ϑ in common, which lines on the line $\alpha\beta$, because ζ and η lie on this line.

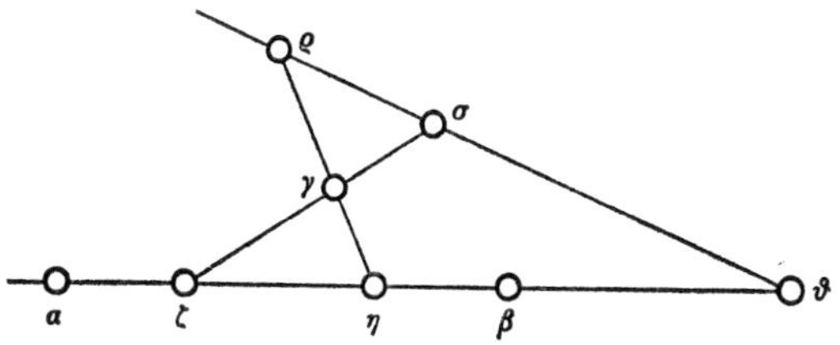

Fig. 37

With the help of symmetry and transitivity the following theorems can be proved in the same way as the theorems 1a–c:

Theorem 2a. Any three linearly independent points determine precisely one plane (by definition).

Theorem 2b. Any four arbitrary points of a plane are always linearly dependent.

Theorem 2c. If the plane contains two distinct points ϱ, σ, then it contains the line $\varrho\sigma$.

The assumptions are:

$$A_4(\alpha,\beta,\gamma,\varrho), \text{ i.e. } \bigvee_{\xi} (A(\alpha,\beta,\xi) \wedge A(\xi,\gamma,\varrho)),$$

$$A_4(\alpha,\beta,\gamma,\sigma), \text{ i.e. } \bigvee_{\eta} (A(\alpha,\beta,\eta) \wedge A(\eta,\gamma,\sigma)).$$

Now let ζ be an arbitrary point of the line $\varrho\sigma$, i.e. $A(\varrho,\sigma,\zeta)$. Then we claim: $A_4(\alpha,\beta,\gamma,\zeta)$, i.e. $\bigvee_{\vartheta} (A(\alpha,\beta,\vartheta) \wedge A(\vartheta,\gamma,\zeta))$.

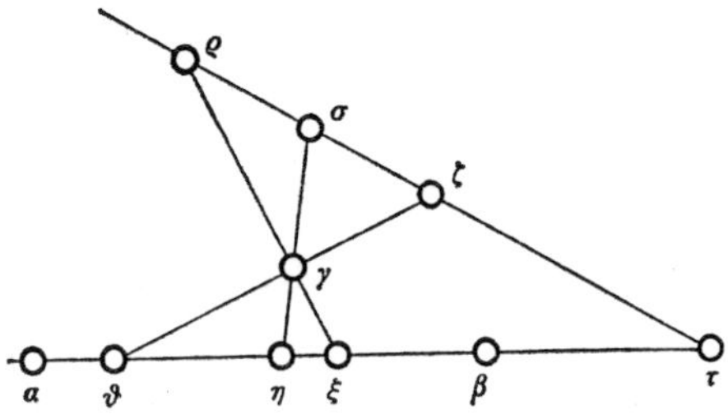

Fig. 38

The proof can be followed in Fig. 38: first of all there exists a point τ as intersection of $\varrho\sigma$ and $\xi\eta=\alpha\beta$. Then for an arbitrary point ζ of the line $\varrho\sigma$ there exists the intersection ϑ of $\zeta\gamma$ and $\alpha\beta=\xi\tau$, because the lines $\tau\zeta$ and $\xi\gamma$ intersect in ϱ.

An immediate consequence of Theorem 2c is:

Theorem 2d. If two planes have two distinct points ϱ, σ in common, then they have the line $\varrho\sigma$ in common.

Further, as in Theorem 1c one proves:

Theorem 2e. If a plane contains three linearly independent points ϱ, σ, τ, then it contains the whole plane $\varrho\sigma\tau$.

Quite generally the linear dependence of $r>3$ points can be defined as follows:

$$A_r(\alpha_1,\ldots,\alpha_r) \Leftrightarrows \bigvee_{\eta} (A_{r-1}(\alpha_1,\ldots,\alpha_{r-2},\eta) \wedge A(\eta,\alpha_{r-1},\alpha_r)).$$

The index on A can be omitted in most cases, because the number of arguments can usually be recognized otherwise. For the sake of completeness we define:

$$A_2(\alpha, \beta) \leftrightharpoons \alpha = \beta.$$

But for convenience, in order to avoid proofs by induction, we shall restrict ourselves to three-dimensional projective space. We achieve this by postulating:

> *Dimension axiom.* There exist four linearly independent points: any five points are linearly dependent.

We mention in passing that the proof of reflexivity, symmetry, and transitivity of A_r even for $r > 4$ does not require any new axioms.

If under the hypothesis $\neg\, A(\alpha, \beta, \gamma, \delta)$, we define

$$l_4(\alpha, \beta, \gamma, \delta) \leftrightharpoons \{\xi;\, A_5(\alpha, \beta, \gamma, \delta, \xi)\},$$

then by the dimension axiom this is the whole set p. We call (p, A) *three-dimensional projective space.*

The dimension axiom implies that a plane $\alpha\beta\gamma$ and a line $\varrho\sigma$ always have a point of intersection; for since five points are always linearly dependent, by the definition of A_5 there exists a point η with $A{>}(\alpha, \beta, \gamma, \eta) \wedge A(\eta, \varrho, \sigma)$.

6.2.3. The lattice of linear subspaces. In the preceding section we established the fundamental theorems that are required for the development of a projective geometry, also for the introduction of coordinates and the transition to a vector space. We shall not dwell on this here in detail. But we shall sketch from our point of view the transition to lattice theory.

To be brief, we define: a subset l of p is called a *linear subspace* of p with respect to the relation A if l contains together with every set of linearly independent points (by the dimension axiom such a set can consist of at most four points) also all points linearly dependent on them.

By what we have proved, the following subsets of p have this property: 1) the empty set, 2) sets consisting of a single point (which we shall also call points), 3) lines, 4) planes, 5) p itself. And these are the only linear subspaces of p.

As usual, we define: a set of points $\alpha_1, \ldots, \alpha_r$ is called a *basis* of l if

$\alpha_1, \ldots, \alpha_r$ are linearly independent and every point of l is linearly dependent on them:

$$\bigwedge_{\xi \in l} A(\alpha_1, \ldots, \alpha_r, \xi).$$

Theorem 3a. If l has a basis of r points, then any r linearly independent points form a basis of l.

For $r=0$ and $r=1$ this is clear, for $r=2$ it is Theorem 1b, for $r=3$ it is Theorem 2, for $r=4$ it follows from the dimension axiom.

Obviously we also have

Theorem 3b. Every set of linearly independent points of l can be supplemented to a basis of l.

By means of these we can now prove:

1) The set L of linear subspaces with the order relation $\subseteq$ forms a lattice $(L, \subseteq)$.

2) $(L, \subseteq)$ is complemented (see § 6.1).

3) In $(L, \subseteq)$ the chain theorem holds; the length of a maximal chain from the null element n (the empty set) to l, in other words the lattice-theoretical dimension $\delta(l)$, is equal to the number of basis elements.

4) The dimension equation holds

$$\delta(a \sqcup b) = \delta(a) + \delta(b) - \delta(a \sqcap b),$$

so that $(L, \subseteq)$ is modular.

We sketch the proof of 4):

$$\begin{aligned} &\text{let } \gamma_1, \ldots, \gamma_t \text{ be a basis of } a \sqcap b, \\ &\gamma_1, \ldots, \gamma_t, \alpha_{t+1}, \ldots, \alpha_r \text{ a basis of } a, \\ &\gamma_1, \ldots, \gamma_t, \beta_{t+1}, \ldots, \beta_s \text{ a basis of } b. \end{aligned}$$

What we have to show is that the points

$$\gamma_1, \ldots, \gamma_t, \alpha_{t+1}, \ldots, \alpha_r, \beta_{t+1}, \ldots, \beta_s \tag{1}$$

are linearly independent; then they form a basis of $a \sqcup b$, and a count of the basis elements of $a \sqcup b, a \sqcap b, a, b$ yields the dimension equation.

If the points (1) were linearly dependent, then there would exist a ξ with

$$A(\gamma_1, \ldots, \beta_{s-2}, \xi) \wedge A(\xi, \beta_{s-1}, \beta_s);$$

then there would also exist an η with

$$A(\gamma_1, \ldots, \beta_{s-3}, \eta) \wedge A(\eta, \beta_{s-2}, \xi) \wedge A(\xi, \beta_{s-1}, \beta_s),$$

hence

$$A(\gamma_1, \ldots, \beta_{s-3}, \eta) \wedge A(\eta, \beta_{s-2}, \beta_{s-1}, \beta_s).$$

Continuation of the method leads to the point ζ for which

$$(2) \qquad A(\gamma_1, \ldots, \alpha_r, \zeta) \wedge A(\zeta, \beta_{t+1}, \ldots, \beta_s)$$

holds. (2) states that ζ belongs to a and b, hence to $a \sqcap b$, i.e. that $A(\gamma_1, \ldots, \gamma_t, \zeta)$ holds. But from

$$A(\gamma_1, \ldots, \gamma_t, \zeta) \wedge A(\zeta, \beta_{t+1}, \ldots, \beta_s)$$

it follows, again by (2), that

$$A(\gamma_1, \ldots, \gamma_t, \beta_{t+1}, \ldots, \beta_s),$$

contradicting the fact that $\gamma_1, \ldots, \gamma_t, \beta_{t+1}, \ldots, \beta_s$ form a basis of b and so are linearly independent.

Thus $(L, \subseteq)$ is a modular complemented lattice of finite length (by the dimension axiom).

6.2.4. Transition from the lattice to geometry. Conversely, if a modular complemented lattice $(V, \leqslant)$ of finite length is given, then every element has a dimension, and the dimension equation holds. One can call the elements of dimension 1, i.e. the atoms, points—they will be denoted again by small Greek letters—and define a relation A as follows:

$$A(\alpha, \beta, \gamma) \leftrightharpoons \alpha \leqslant \beta \sqcup \gamma \vee \beta \leqslant \gamma \sqcup \alpha \vee \gamma \leqslant \alpha \sqcup \beta.$$

We have to prove this relation satisfies (*r*), (*s*), (*t*), (*q*).

The validity of (*r*) and (*s*) is immediately clear.

The fact that the definition of A contains three statements connected by $\vee$ is inconvenient for the remaining proofs. So we make the following observations:

1) If $\alpha \neq \beta$, then $\delta(\alpha \sqcup \beta) = 2$; for α and β have the common lower neighbour n, hence the common upper neighbour $\alpha \sqcup \beta$.

2) $A(\alpha, \beta, \gamma)$ holds if and only if $\delta(\alpha \sqcup \beta \sqcup \gamma) \leqslant 2$.

3) Since $\delta(\alpha \sqcup \beta \sqcup \gamma) \geqslant \delta(\alpha \sqcup \beta)$, $\alpha \neq \beta \wedge A(\alpha, \beta, \gamma)$ holds if and only if $\delta(\alpha \sqcup \beta \sqcup \gamma) = \delta(\alpha \sqcup \beta) = 2$, i.e. if $\gamma \leqslant \alpha \sqcup \beta$.

Accordingly (*t*) states (see page 104):

$$\alpha \neq \beta \wedge \xi \leqslant \alpha \sqcup \beta \wedge \eta \leqslant \alpha \sqcup \beta \rightarrow \\ \alpha \leqslant \xi \sqcup \eta \vee \xi \leqslant \eta \sqcup \alpha \vee \eta \leqslant \alpha \sqcup \xi.$$

If $\xi=\eta$, the two last statements are valid;
if $\xi\neq\eta$, then (i): $\delta(\xi \sqcup \eta)=2=\delta(\alpha \sqcup \beta)$.
The assumptions imply (ii): $\xi \sqcup \eta \leqslant \alpha \sqcup \beta$.
From (i) and (ii) it follows that $\xi \sqcup \eta=\alpha \sqcup \beta$, i.e. $\alpha \leqslant \xi \sqcup \eta$.

(q) states:

$$A(\alpha,\beta,\xi) \wedge A(\gamma,\vartheta,\xi) \rightarrow \bigvee_{\eta} (A(\alpha,\gamma,\eta) \wedge A(\beta,\vartheta,\eta)).$$

If $\alpha=\beta$ or $\beta=\vartheta$, then $\eta=\alpha$ satisfies the requirements;
if $\alpha=\gamma$ or $\gamma=\vartheta$, then $\eta=\vartheta$ satisfies the requirements.
Hence we may assume that $\alpha\neq\beta$, $\gamma\neq\vartheta$, $\alpha\neq\gamma$, $\beta\neq\vartheta$.
Then the assumption is: $\delta[(\alpha \sqcup \beta) \sqcap (\gamma \sqcup \vartheta)]\geqslant 1$
and the assertion: $\delta[(\alpha \sqcup \gamma) \sqcap (\beta \sqcup \vartheta)]\geqslant 1$.
By the dimension equation we have

$$\delta[(\alpha \sqcup \beta) \sqcap (\gamma \sqcup \vartheta)] = \delta(\alpha \sqcup \beta)+\delta(\gamma \sqcup \vartheta)-\delta(\alpha \sqcup \beta \sqcup \gamma \sqcup \vartheta).$$

Then from the assumption and $\delta(\alpha \sqcup \beta)=\delta(\gamma \sqcup \vartheta)=2$ it follows that

$$\delta(\alpha \sqcup \beta \sqcup \gamma \sqcup \vartheta) \leqslant 3.$$

Hence

$$\begin{aligned}\delta[(\alpha \sqcup \gamma) \sqcap (\beta \sqcup \vartheta)] &= \delta(\alpha \sqcup \gamma)+\delta(\beta \sqcup \vartheta)-\delta(\alpha \sqcup \beta \sqcup \gamma \sqcup \vartheta)\\ &\geqslant \quad 2 \quad + \quad 2 \quad - \quad 3 \quad = \quad 1.\end{aligned}$$

For a given V a lattice L can be built up on the set of points of V, as explained in § 6.2.3. It is easy to see that L is isomorphic to a sublattice of V. That L is isomorphic to V itself can be seen as follows: every element of L is a union of points of V. We shall show later (Chapter VII, § 1.4) that every element of V, too, can be represented as a union of points. This then is the one-to-one correspondence between L and V.

6.3. Orthocomplement

The complement of an element is uniquely determined only in distributive complemented lattices (see Chapter VI, § 1.3, Theorem IV, page 121). But even in more general complemented lattices a definite complement can occasionally be singled out from the complements of an element, as in the case of subspaces of a vector space, provided an orthogonality condition is defined in it, for example, by a bilinear form.

Let e be the vector space over the field $\Omega = \boldsymbol{R}$ of real numbers. (If Ω is the field of complex numbers, a few modifications are necessary.) A *bilinear form* is a mapping of $e \times e$ into Ω, i.e. it assigns to every pair $\mathfrak{x}$, $\mathfrak{y}$ of vectors an element $\Gamma(\mathfrak{x},\mathfrak{y}) \in \Omega$. Bilinearity is characterized by the following properties:

$$\Gamma(\sigma\mathfrak{x},\mathfrak{y}) = \sigma\cdot\Gamma(\mathfrak{x},\mathfrak{y}), \quad \Gamma(\mathfrak{x},\tau\mathfrak{y}) = \tau\cdot\Gamma(\mathfrak{x},\mathfrak{y}); \quad (\sigma,\tau \in \Omega).$$
$$\Gamma(\mathfrak{x}_1+\mathfrak{x}_2,\mathfrak{y}) = \Gamma(\mathfrak{x}_1,\mathfrak{y})+\Gamma(\mathfrak{x}_2,\mathfrak{y}),$$
$$\Gamma(\mathfrak{x},\mathfrak{y}_1+\mathfrak{y}_2) = \Gamma(\mathfrak{x},\mathfrak{y}_1)+\Gamma(\mathfrak{x},\mathfrak{y}_2).$$

Suppose that we are given such a mapping which in addition is *symmetric*, i.e. for which $\Gamma(\mathfrak{x},\mathfrak{y}) = \Gamma(\mathfrak{y},\mathfrak{x})$ and whose associated quadratic form is *positive definite*, i.e.

$$\Gamma(\mathfrak{x},\mathfrak{x}) \geqslant 0, \quad = 0 \text{ only for } \mathfrak{x} = \mathfrak{o}.$$

Then a basis $\mathfrak{e}_1,\ldots,\mathfrak{e}_k$ can be chosen in such a way that in the coordinates ξ_κ, η_κ relative to this basis

$$\Gamma(\mathfrak{x},\mathfrak{y}) = \xi_1\eta_1+\ldots+\xi_k\eta_k.$$

The vector $\mathfrak{x}$ is said to be *orthogonal* to the vector $\mathfrak{y}$ if $\Gamma(\mathfrak{x},\mathfrak{y}) = 0$.

Symmetry implies: if $\mathfrak{x}$ is orthogonal to $\mathfrak{y}$, then $\mathfrak{y}$ is also orthogonal to $\mathfrak{x}$. Definiteness implies that only the null vector is orthogonal to itself. The conditions of linearity imply that the vectors orthogonal to all the vectors of a subspace x form a subspace: we denote it by x'. In this way a mapping $x \rightarrowtail x'$ is given if the lattice $\mathfrak{L}e$ of subspaces of e, with the properties:

(1) $$x \sqcup x' = e; \quad x \sqcap x' = n,$$

(2) $$x'' = x,$$

(3) $$x \leqslant y \rightarrow y' \leqslant x'.$$

> *Definition.* If a mapping with the properties (1)–(3) is given in a lattice, then the lattice is said to be *orthocomplemented*, and x' is called the orthocomplement of x.

Examples of orthocomplemented lattices are given in Fig. 39.

Orthogonal complemented modular lattices have a certain significance for quantum mechanics.[1] A state of a physical system can be described in classical physics by a point in the phase space, in

[1] The fundamental paper is: G. Birkhoff and J. v. Neumann, 'The Logic of Quantum Mechanics', *Annals of Math.* **37** (1936), 823–843.

quantum mechanics by a vector in a Hilbert space. A Hilbert space is a vector space of countable dimension; the complications that arise from the infinite dimension cannot be discussed here, without a detailed treatment of the concept 'Hilbert space'.

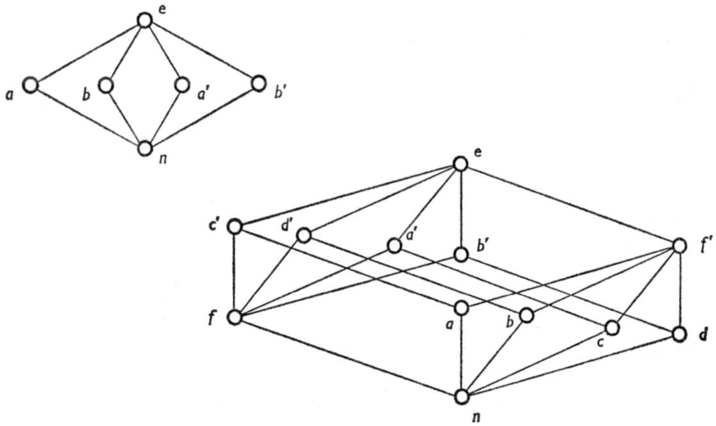

Fig. 39

A property of a physical system or, what comes to the same thing, a statement about a physical system (namely the statement that the system has a certain property) is represented in classical mechanics by an (arbitrary) point set of the phase space, in quantum mechanics by a subspace of the Hilbert space. If a and b are such subspaces, then

$a \subseteq b$ means: 'the statement a implies the statement b',

$a \sqcap b$ means: the statement 'a and b',

$a \sqcup b$ means: the statement 'a or b',

a' means: the statement 'complementary' to a.

Here, what corresponds to 'or' is not union, but the smallest subspace containing a and b, and the complementary statement is not precisely the same as classical negation. Therefore the rules for this 'quantum logic' differ from those of classical propositional logic; they are not those of a Boolean, i.e. complemented distributive lattice, but those of an orthocomplemented modular lattice.

We note a few rules of such a lattice.

1) The *formulae of de Morgan* hold:

$$(a \sqcap b)' = a' \sqcup b'; \quad (a \sqcup b)' = a' \sqcap b'.$$

Proof. (i) $a \sqcap b \leqslant a$, hence $a' \leqslant (a \sqcap b)'$,

$a \sqcap b \leqslant b$, hence $b' \leqslant (a \sqcap b)'$,

and so $a' \sqcup b' \leqslant (a \sqcap b)'$.

(ii) $a \leqslant a \sqcup b$, hence $(a \sqcup b)' \leqslant a'$,

$b \leqslant a \sqcup b$, hence $(a \sqcup b)' \leqslant b'$,

and so $(a \sqcup b)' \leqslant a' \sqcap b'$.

But $a \sqcap b = (a \sqcap b)'' \leqslant (a' \sqcup b')'$ by (i) and (2)

$\leqslant a'' \sqcap b''$ by (ii)

$= a \sqcap b$ by (2).

Thus we always have $=$ instead of $\leqslant$.

2) In classical propositional logic implication is connected with subjunction as follows: a implies b if $a \mathbin{\ulcorner\!\!-} b$ is true; in lattice-theoretical notation

$$a \leqslant b \leftrightarrow a \mathbin{\ulcorner\!\!-} b = e.$$

In a Boolean lattice $a \mathbin{\ulcorner\!\!-} b = a^0 \sqcup b$ (if a^0 is the complement of a).

Is it possible in an orthocomplemented modular lattice to assign to implication an operation—denoted by $\curvearrowright$—such that

$$a \leqslant b \leftrightarrow a \curvearrowright b = e$$

holds?[1]

First of all, the operation $a' \sqcup b$ does not satisfy the requirements. True, we have $a \leqslant b \rightarrow a' \sqcup b = e$; this follows from $a' \sqcup a = e$ and $a \leqslant b$. But $a' \sqcup b = e \rightarrow a \leqslant b$ does not always hold; we have only to choose for b a complement to a' different from a. One finds examples in Fig. 39.

But if we set $a \curvearrowright b \leftrightharpoons a' \sqcup (a \sqcap b)$, then

(i) $a \leqslant b \rightarrow a \sqcap b = a \rightarrow a' \sqcup (a \sqcap b) = a' \sqcup a = e.$

(ii) If $e = a' \sqcup (a \sqcap b)$, then

$a = a \sqcap [a' \sqcup (a \sqcap b)]$

$= (a \sqcap a') \sqcup (a \sqcap b)$ by the modular law

$= a \sqcap b$, because $a' \sqcap a = n$.

Now one can base quantum logic on laws for this subjunction, as is shown in detail in the paper by Kunsemüller quoted above.

Note. In a distributive lattice

$$a' \sqcup (a \sqcap b) = (a' \sqcup a) \sqcap (a' \sqcup b) = a' \sqcup b.$$

[1] H. Kunsemüller, 'Zur logischen Deutung der Quantenmechanik', *Diss. phil.* Hamburg, 1959.

CHAPTER VI

Distributive Lattices

§ 1. General statements

1.1. Definition

A lattice V is said to be *distributive* if for all its elements

$$a \sqcap (b \sqcup c) = (a \sqcap b) \sqcup (a \sqcap c), \tag{D1}$$

$$a \sqcup (b \sqcap c) = (a \sqcup b) \sqcap (a \sqcup c). \tag{D2}$$

As an immediate consequence of the definition we have:

Corollary 1. If $(V, \sqcap, \sqcup)$ is distributive, then so is every sub-lattice.

Corollary 2. If the lattices $V_1, \ldots, V_r$ are distributive, then so is the direct product $V_1 \times V_2 \times \ldots \times V_r$; the same holds for an infinite number of factors.

Of the two relations (D1) and (D2) each follows from the other. For example, if (D1) holds, then we have

$$\begin{aligned}(a \sqcup b) \sqcap (a \sqcup c) &= ((a \sqcup b) \sqcap a) \sqcup ((a \sqcup b) \sqcap c) \quad \text{by (D1)}\\ &= a \sqcup ((a \sqcap c) \sqcup (b \sqcap c)) \quad \text{by the absorption law and (D1)}\\ &= a \sqcup (b \sqcap c) \quad \text{by the associative and the absorption law.}\end{aligned}$$

Moreover, in every lattice

$$(a \sqcap b) \sqcup (a \sqcap c) \leqslant a \sqcap (b \sqcup c),$$

for

$$a \sqcap b \leqslant a, \quad a \sqcap c \leqslant a$$

as well as

$$a \sqcap b \leqslant b \sqcup c, \quad a \sqcap c \leqslant b \sqcup c.$$

Similarly one proves that

$$a \sqcup (b \sqcap c) \leqslant (a \sqcup b) \sqcap (a \sqcup c).$$

Hence, in order to demonstrate that a lattice is distributive, one has only to prove one of the following two inequalities:

(D1u) $$a \sqcap (b \sqcup c) \leqslant (a \sqcap b) \sqcup (a \sqcap c),$$

(D2u) $$a \sqcup (b \sqcap c) \geqslant (a \sqcup b) \sqcap (a \sqcup c).$$

1.2. Examples

1) Propositions with the connectives $\wedge$ and $\vee$, defined by the truth table CL, page 13, form a distributive lattice (see page 14).

2) The lattice $\mathfrak{P}e$ of all subsets of a set e with the operations $\cap$, $\cup$ is distributive.

Proof. By definition

$$\xi \in a \cap (b \cup c) \text{ if } \xi \in a \wedge (\xi \in b \vee \xi \in c).$$

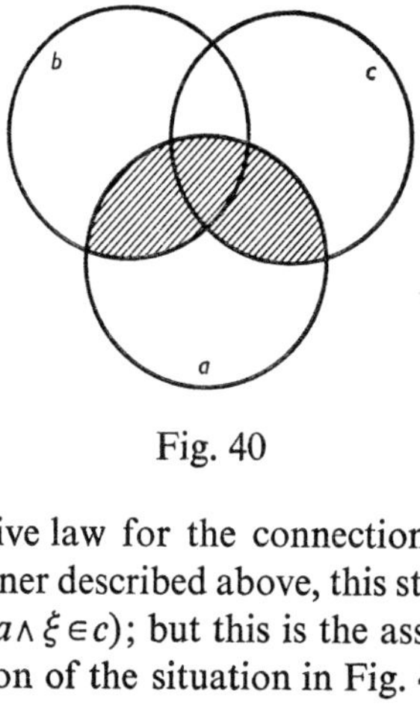

Fig. 40

Since the distributive law for the connection of propositions can be proved in the manner described above, this statement is equivalent to $(\xi \in a \wedge \xi \in b) \vee (\xi \in a \wedge \xi \in c)$; but this is the assertion. One can give an intuitive illustration of the situation in Fig. 40.

3) Every linearly ordered set is a distributive lattice.

Proof. We denote the larger of the two elements x, y by $\max(x,y)$, the smaller one by $\min(x,y)$.
For $x=y$ let $\max(x,y)=\min(x,y)=x=y$.

Then we have in a linearly ordered set

$$a \sqcap (b \sqcup c) = \min(a, \max(b,c)),$$
$$(a \sqcap b) \sqcup (a \sqcap c) = \max(\min(a,b), \min(a,c)).$$

One has to check for the various possible positions of a, b, c whether these elements are equal. Since b and c occur with equal status, we may assume $b \leqslant c$. We have to check three cases

$$a \leqslant b \leqslant c; \quad b \leqslant a \leqslant c; \quad b \leqslant c \leqslant a.$$

Their verification leads to the desired conclusion.

4) By 3) and Corollary 2 the direct product of linearly ordered sets is a distributive lattice. Since the lattice $(N, |)$ of natural numbers with 'divides' as order is a sub-lattice of such a direct product (see Chapter III, § 2.2), by Corollary 1 $(N, |)$ is distributive.

1.3. Laws of computation

If $c \leqslant a$, i.e. $a \sqcap c = c$, then (D1) yields

$$c \leqslant a \rightarrow a \sqcap (b \sqcup c) = (a \sqcap b) \sqcup c;$$

Thus, the modular law is a consequence of the distributive law.

Theorem I. Every distributive lattice is modular.

The fact that not every modular lattice is distributive, is shown by the order diagram $(\bar{d})$ Fig. 41, which incidentally represents the lattice of subgroups of the Klein Four group. (As this group is commutative, the subgroups are normal.)

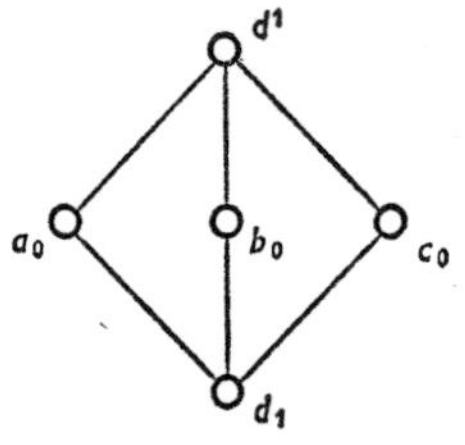

Fig. 41 $(\bar{d})$

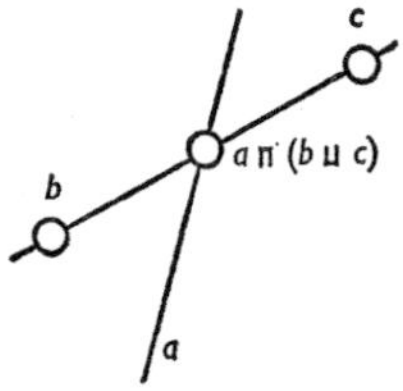

Fig. 42

Also the linear subspaces of (three-dimensional) projective space form a modular lattice (see Chapter V, § 4, § 6.2) that is not distributive. One can choose, for example, a as a line, b and c as points not on a, but so that the lines a and $b \sqcup c$ intersect (Fig. 42).

The example $(\bar{d})$ is characteristic in the following sense:

Theorem II. Every modular, non-distributive lattice contains a sub-lattice with the order diagram $(\bar{d})$.

To save brackets we write here ab instead of $a \sqcap b$. For the proof we use

Theorem III. If we set

$$d_1 = ab \sqcup bc \sqcup ca,$$
$$d^1 = (a \sqcup b)(b \sqcup c)(c \sqcup a),$$

then $d_1 = d^1$ holds if and only if V is distributive.

Proof. 1) The distributive law implies $d_1 = d^1$ by 'multiplying out'.

2) $d_1 = d^1$ implies first of all the modular law. For if $a \geqslant c$ is assumed, then

$$ab \geqslant bc,\ ca = c, \text{ hence } d_1 = ab \sqcup c,$$

and $a \sqcup b \geqslant b \sqcup c$ and $c \sqcup a = a$, hence $d^1 = a(b \sqcup c)$.

In order to prove the distributive law we now form

$$a \sqcup d_1 = a \sqcup bc.$$

This is

$$= a \sqcup d^1 = a \sqcup (a \sqcup b)(b \sqcup c)(c \sqcup a).$$

Since $a \leqslant c \sqcup a$, by the modular law this is

$$= [a \sqcup (a \sqcup b)(b \sqcup c)](c \sqcup a),$$

and since $a \leqslant a \sqcup b$, again by (m2)

$$= (a \sqcup b \sqcup c)(a \sqcup b)(c \sqcup a) = (a \sqcup b)(c \sqcup a).$$

For the proof of Theorem II we prove first of all the

Lemma. In every modular lattice the elements d_1, d^1 and

$$a_0 = (bc \sqcup a)(b \sqcup c) = (b \sqcup c)a \sqcup bc,$$
$$b_0 = (ca \sqcup b)(c \sqcup a) = (c \sqcup a)b \sqcup ca,$$
$$c_0 = (ab \sqcup c)(a \sqcup b) = (a \sqcup b)c \sqcup ab$$

form a sub-lattice.

Note. These equations follow from (m2).

Proof. 1) $d_1 \leqslant a_0$, for

$$ab \leqslant a(b \sqcup c) \leqslant a_0,$$
$$bc \leqslant a_0,$$
$$ca \leqslant (b \sqcup c)a \leqslant a_0.$$

Similarly, or dually, one proves:

$$(1)\qquad \begin{aligned} d_1 &\leqslant a_0 \leqslant d^1, \\ d_1 &\leqslant b_0 \leqslant d^1, \\ d_1 &\leqslant c_0 \leqslant d^1. \end{aligned}$$

2) It has to be shown that together with any two elements of $\bar{D}=\{a_0, b_0, c_0, d^1, d_1\}$ their combinations by $\sqcap$ and $\sqcup$ also belong to $\bar{D}$. By virtue of (1) and for reasons of symmetry it is sufficient to prove $a_0 \sqcup b_0 = d^1$.

$$a_0 \sqcup b_0 = (b \sqcup c)a \sqcup bc \sqcup (c \sqcup a)b \sqcup ca = (b \sqcup c)a \sqcup (c \sqcup a)b = z.$$

Now we have $b \sqcup c \geqslant b \geqslant (c \sqcup a)b$, hence the modular law implies

$$z = (b \sqcup c)(a \sqcup (c \sqcup a)b),$$

and since $a \leqslant c \sqcup a$, it follows again from (m2) that

$$z = (b \sqcup c)(c \sqcup a)(a \sqcup b) = d^1.$$

So the Lemma is proved.

In a non-distributive lattice there are three elements a, b, c for which $d_1 \neq d^1$. Now we show: if $d_1 \neq d^1$, then the five elements of $\bar{D}$ are distinct from one another and their order relations are represented by $(\bar{d})$ (Fig. 41, page 118). This then will prove Theorem II.

1) $$a_0 \neq b_0,\ b_0 \neq c_0,\ c_0 \neq a_0.$$

If $a_0 = b_0$, then also $d_1 = a_0 b_0 = a_0 \sqcup b_0 = d^1$.

2) If $a_0 = d^1$, then by (1) we would have $b_0 \leqslant a_0$ and $c_0 \leqslant a_0$, hence $b_0 = b_0 a_0 = d_1 = c_0 a_0 = c_0$, in contradiction to 1). From symmetry and duality it follows that all the five elements of $\bar{D}$ are distinct from one another.

The proof of 2) also shows that $b_0 \nleqslant a_0$, for otherwise we would have $b_0 \sqcup a_0 = a_0 = d^1$. The same holds for an arbitrary pair of the elements a_0, b_0, c_0. This and (1) states that the order relations are in fact those of $(\bar{d})$.

In ordinary algebra the distributive law can be used to remove brackets, i.e., to represent an algebraic expression as a sum of products. In a distributive lattice an expression built up by the operations $\sqcup$, $\sqcap$ can be represented as a conjunction of adjunctions or as an adjunction of conjunctions. (We use the nomenclature of logic, because this representation has a particularly important application in logic.) An adjunctive representation is of the form

$$p = a_1 \sqcup a_2 \sqcup \ldots \sqcup a_n,$$

where each a_i contains only the operation $\sqcap$,

$$a_i = a_{i1} \sqcap a_{i2} \sqcap \ldots \sqcap a_{im_i};$$

If one writes ab instead of $a \sqcap b$, then the formation of an adjunctive representation is a familiar calculation. But if one wants to *prove* that every formula can be represented adjunctively, then one has to face the difficulty of giving a description of this customary calculating process.

For example, what is the salient point in the transition from

$$c(d \vee a(b \vee c)) \text{ to } c(d \vee ab \vee ac)?$$

It is: that a $\vee$-symbol is 'liberated' from a bracket.

But how can this be described exactly? Here it seems to me that a symbolism due to Łukasiewicz is useful; a symbolism which we shall now demonstrate in an example.

Łukasiewicz writes Kab for $a \wedge b$, Aab for $a \vee b$. This permits a notation free of brackets. For example

$$c(d \vee a(b \vee c)) = KcAdKaAbc.$$

The associative law takes the form

$$a \vee (b \vee c) = AaAbc = AAabc = (a \vee b) \vee c.$$

Hence an adjunctive representation can be characterized by the fact that all the A stand at the beginning of the formula. Now the distributive law

$$KaAbc = AKabKac$$

has precisely the effect that a sequence $K \ldots A \ldots$ goes over into the sequence $AK \ldots K \ldots$.

The completion of the proof is left to the reader.

Theorem IV. In a distributive lattice the cancellation law holds: from $a \sqcap b = a \sqcap c$ and $a \sqcup b = a \sqcup c$ it follows that $b = c$.

Proof. We use the absorption law, the distributive law, and the assumptions

$$\begin{aligned} b = b \sqcup (a \sqcap b) = b \sqcup (a \sqcap c) &= (b \sqcup a) \sqcap (b \sqcup c) \\ &= (a \sqcup c) \sqcap (b \sqcup c) \\ &= (a \sqcap b) \sqcup c \\ &= (a \sqcap c) \sqcup c = c. \end{aligned}$$

That this theorem cannot hold, in general, in a modular but non-distributive lattice is shown by the example $(\bar{d})$.

Only if one makes the *additional assumption* $b \leqslant c$, then we have, by the modular law,

$$b = b \sqcup (a \sqcap c) = c \sqcap (a \sqcup b) = c \sqcap (a \sqcup c) = c.$$

In a modular lattice the cancellation law holds under the additional assumption $b \leqslant c$.

From Theorem IV it follows that: in a distributive lattice an element can have at most one complement, or relative complement, in an interval.

Conversely: if the cancellation law holds in a lattice V, then V is distributive.

If it were not distributive, then it would contain a sublattice $(\bar{m})$ or $(\bar{d})$, i.e., triplets a, b, c for which the cancellation law does not hold.

This has the following consequence:

If V is relatively complemented and if every relative complement is uniquely determined, then V is distributive. A lattice that is distributive and complemented is called a *Boolean lattice*.

1.4. Distributivity in complete lattices

A complete lattice V is said to be *fully distributive* (if a distinction is necessary: $\sqcap$-fully distributive) if for every element $a \in V$ and every subset $M \subseteq V$:

(vD) $$a \sqcap \bigsqcup_{x \in M} x = \bigsqcup_{x \in M} a \sqcap x.$$

The dual law will not be needed for the time being. It suffices that for every subset $M \subseteq V$ the upper limit $\bigsqcup_M x$ exists in V; V will then be called $\sqcup$-*complete.*

Every fully distributive lattice is distributive; to prove this one need only choose $M = (b, c)$. Conversely, one shows by mathematical induction that every finite distributive lattice is fully distributive. An infinite complete distributive lattice, however, need not be fully distributive.

As an example consider the lattice with the order diagram of Fig. 43. It is constructed as follows: the set of natural numbers is linearly ordered by magnitude, and is therefore a distributive lattice. So is the lattice consisting of the elements 1 and a with $1 < a$, therefore also the direct product V_0 of the two lattices is distributive. To V_0 we adjoin an element e by postulating: $\bigwedge_{x \in V_0} x < e$.

The lattice V so obtained is obviously complete. That it is distributive one can see as follows: every triplet of elements V_0 is distributive, and in the cases when at least one of the elements is equal to e, the relation $a \sqcap (b \sqcup c) = (a \sqcap b) \sqcup (a \sqcap c)$ is easily verified. If M is the set of elements 1, 2, 3,... without e, then $a \sqcap \bigsqcup_{x \in M} x = a \sqcap e = a$; on the other hand,

$$\bigwedge_{x \in M} a \sqcap x = 1, \text{ hence } \bigsqcup_{x \in M} a \sqcap x = 1.$$

So V is not fully distributive.[1]

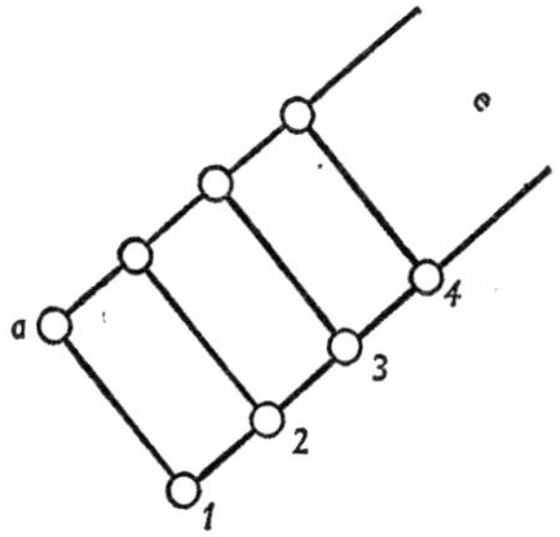

Fig. 43

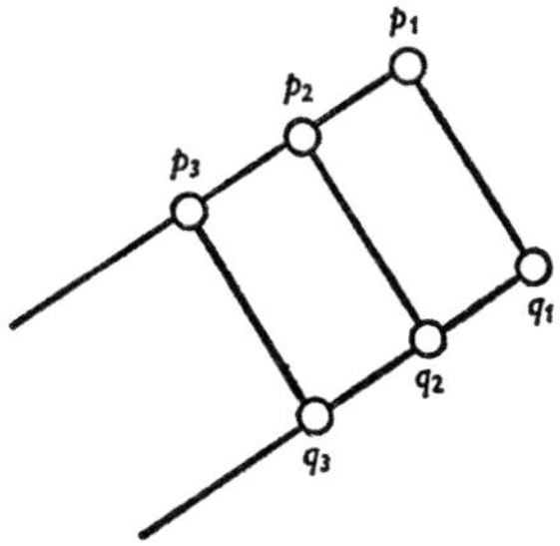

Fig. 44

But the dual statement $a \sqcup \bigsqcap_{x \in M} x = \bigsqcap_{x \in M} a \sqcup x$ holds in V or, what is the same thing, the dual lattice represented in Fig. 44 is fully distributive.

Proof. Suppose that $M \subseteq V$ and that p_k is the largest p contained in M, q_l the largest q contained in M. Then evidently (for a justification we refer to the figure) we have $\bigsqcup_M x = p_k \sqcup q$ and

(1) $$a \sqcap \bigsqcup_M x = a \sqcap (p_k \sqcup q_l) = (a \sqcap p_k) \sqcup (a \sqcap q_l).$$

Furthermore: for every $x \in M$ we have $x \leqslant p_k$ or $x \leqslant q_l$. This implies $a \sqcap x \leqslant (a \sqcap p_k) \sqcup (a \sqcap q_l)$,

(2) $$\bigsqcup_M a \sqcap x \leqslant (a \sqcap p_k) \sqcup (a \sqcap q_l).$$

On the other hand, $p_k \in M$ and $q_l \in M$, hence

(3) $$(a \sqcap p_k) \sqcup (a \sqcap q_l) \leqslant \bigsqcup_M a \sqcap x.$$

[1] This example is a modification of the one given by Hermes, § 24, page 129.

The assertion follows from (1), (2), and (3).

Note. Here it is immaterial whether or not the lattice is completed by a smallest element.

In every $\bigsqcup$-complete lattice

$$a \sqcap x \leqslant a,\ a \sqcap x \leqslant \bigsqcup_{x\in M} x, \text{ hence } \bigsqcup_{x\in M} (a \sqcap x) \leqslant a \sqcap \bigsqcup_{x\in M} x.$$

To check full distributivity, one has only to verify

$$\text{(vDu)} \qquad a \sqcap \bigsqcup_{x\in M} x \leqslant \bigsqcup_{x\in M} (a \sqcap x).$$

Every *complemented* $\bigsqcup$-complete distributive lattice (i.e. every complete Boolean lattice) is fully distributive.

Proof. We abbreviate $\bigsqcup_{x\in M} (a \sqcap x) = u$.

Then for all $x \in M$:

$$a \sqcap x \leqslant u,$$

$$(a \sqcap x) \sqcup a^0 \leqslant u \sqcup a^0.$$

By the distributive law and since $a \sqcup a^0 = e$, this implies

$$x \sqcup a^0 \leqslant u \sqcup a^0,$$

hence

$$x \leqslant u \sqcup a^0,$$

$$\bigsqcup_{x\in M} x \leqslant u \sqcup a^0,$$

$$a \sqcap \bigsqcup_{x\in M} x \leqslant a \sqcap (u \sqcup a^0) = a \sqcap u \leqslant u.$$

The fact that full distributivity is something distinct from simple distributivity can be illustrated if one observes that the formation of the upper limit is similar to passing to the limit in analysis. Correspondingly one calls a mapping $(x \rightarrowtail f(x))$ of a complete lattice into itself *continuous* if

$$f(\bigsqcup_{x\in M} x) = \bigsqcup_{x\in M} f(x).$$

The lattice is fully distributive if and only if for every $a \in V$ the mapping $x \rightarrowtail a \sqcap x$ is continuous.

The definition of full distributivity contains only $\bigwedge$-quantifiers ($\bigwedge_{a\in V}$, $\bigwedge_{M\subseteq V}$), and is therefore restriction hereditary. Every $\bigsqcup$-complete sublattice $U \subseteq V$ is therefore fully distributive. But here it is essential that the upper limit of a set M in V is the same as in U, and that the lower limit of two elements in V is the same as in the U. This is what is meant by the words '$\sqcup$-complete sublattice'.

§ 2. Brouwer or subjunctive lattices

2.1. Definition. Characteristic properties

In the introduction a *Brouwer* or *subjunctive lattice* was defined as a lattice V with the property:

(Br) For any two elements a and b there exists an element c such that

(1a) $$\bigwedge_{x \in V} x \sqcap a \leqslant b \rightarrow x \leqslant c$$

and

(1b) $$\bigwedge_{x \in V} x \leqslant c \rightarrow x \sqcap a \leqslant b.$$

We proved (page 18) that for a and b there can be only one such element; this was denoted by $a \sqsubset b$. (1a, 1b) then become

(1a′) $$\bigwedge_{x \in V} x \sqcap a \leqslant b \rightarrow x \leqslant a \sqsubset b,$$

(1b′) $$\bigwedge_{x \in V} x \leqslant a \sqsubset b \rightarrow x \sqcap a \leqslant b.$$

Consequences. 1) Let us put $a = b$. Since $x \sqcap a \leqslant a$ for all $x \in V$, we have $\bigwedge_{x \in V} x \leqslant a \sqsubset a$.

Thus, a subjunctive lattice has a unit element e, and since a lattice can contain at most one unit element, we have for arbitrary a and b

(2) $$a \sqsubset a = b \sqsubset b = e.$$

2) Since $a \sqsubset b \leqslant a \sqsubset b$, it follows from (1b′) that:

(3) $$a \sqcap (a \sqsubset b) \leqslant b.$$

3) (1a′) states that $a \sqsubset b$ is an upper bound of the set

$$S_{ab} = \{x;\, x \sqcap a \leqslant b\}.$$

From (1b′) (for $x = a \sqsubset b$) it follows that this upper bound belongs to S_{ab}, and is therefore its upper limit.

Thus, in a subjunctive lattice each of the sets S_{ab} has an upper limit v_{ab}, and $v_{ab} \in S_{ab}$.

But this is characteristic of subjunctive lattices: if in a lattice V

each of the sets S_{ab} has an upper limit and this belongs to S_{ab}, then V is subjunctive.

Proof. 1) c is the upper limit of S_{ab}, and so (1a) is satisfied.

2) If $c \in S_{ab}$, then $c \sqcap a \leqslant b$ and so for every $x \leqslant c$:

$$x \sqcap a \leqslant c \sqcap a \leqslant b, \text{ whence (1b) holds.}$$

If V is not subjunctive, then the upper limit of S_{ab} need not exist, and if it exists it need not belong to S_{ab}. In the lattice represented by Fig. 45, the upper limit of $S_{ab}=\{n,b,c\}$ is e.

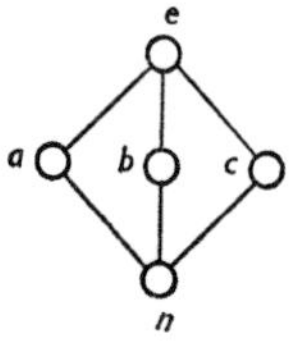

Fig. 45

The upper limits $v_{ab}=\bigsqcup_{Sab} x$ of all S_{ab} certainly exist if V is complete relative to $\sqcup$. We claim that $v_{ab} \in S_{ab}$ if and only if V is fully distributive, in other words: *A $\sqcup$-complete lattice is subjunctive if and only if it is fully distributive.*

Proof. 1) Let V be fully distributive. We claim that $v_{ab} \in S_{ab}$, i.e. $a \sqcap \bigsqcup_{Sab} x \leqslant b$.

By virtue of full distributivity we have $a \sqcap \bigsqcup_{Sab} x = \bigsqcup_{Sab}(a \sqcap x)$, and this element is $\leqslant b$; for we have $x \sqcap a \leqslant b$ for every x in S_{ab}.

2) Let V be subjunctive. We claim that for an arbitrary subset $M \subseteq V$:

$$a \sqcap \bigsqcup_M x \leqslant \bigsqcup_M (a \sqcap x).$$

If we set $\bigsqcup_M a \sqcap x = b$, then for every $x \in M$: $a \sqcap x \leqslant b$, and so $x \leqslant a \sqsubset b$, and therefore $\bigsqcup_M x \leqslant a \sqsubset b$, whence

$$a \sqcap \bigsqcup_M x \leqslant a \sqcap (a \sqsubset b) \leqslant b \qquad \text{(by (3)).}$$

Note. The fact that *every subjunctive lattice is distributive* was proved in the introduction. But *a distributive lattice need not be subjunctive*; for as we have seen above, there exist complete distributive lattices that are not fully distributive.

But from what we have proved it follows that: *every finite distributive lattice is subjunctive.*

So we have at our disposal convenient examples of subjunctive lattices, for example, the lattice of divisors of 12 (Fig. 8, page 49). They show among other things that a subjunctive lattice need not be complemented.

2.2. Negation. Pseudo-complement

In the logical interpretation of a subjunctive lattice the meaning of $a \leqslant b$ (which was denoted by $a < b$ in the Introduction) is: the proposition a implies the proposition b (from a follows b). In lattice-theoretical terms we have so far only talked of implication, conjunction, adjunction, and subjunction; subjunction is characterized by 'x implies $a \sqcap\!\!- b$ if and only if $x \wedge a$ implies the proposition b'. But of truth, falsity and negation so far we have not given any account within the framework of lattice theory.

Now every subjunctive lattice contains an element $e = a \sqcap\!\!- a$ with the property $\bigwedge_x x \leqslant e$, i.e., in the logical interpretation: every proposition implies e. We may designate this proposition, which is, as it were, true provided any proposition is true, as 'the truth'. (That only one such proposition occurs is due to the fact that $a = b$ is explained by $a \leqslant b \wedge b \leqslant a$.) However, a subjunctive lattice need not contain a null element; this is shown by the example of the $\sqcup$-complete fully distributive lattice of Fig. 44, page 123. (But see the end of this section.)

That V need not be complemented was mentioned above, so we cannot introduce negation as a complement (as in the Introduction, § 2).

In order to introduce negation by means of subjunction we choose a proposition that appears absurd to us; we denote it by f and define the negation a' of the proposition a by $a' \leftrightharpoons a \sqcap\!\!- f$. In practice we like to choose for f the proposition: I eat my hat (i.e. for $a \sqcap\!\!- f$: if a holds, I eat my hat).

For the algebraic treatment we take an *arbitrary* element of V for f and define a mapping $a \rightarrowtail a'$ by $a' = a \sqcap\!\!- f$. a' is called a *pseudo-complement* of a relative to f.

We look for the relation between a and a', and for the relations between this mapping and the lattice operations.

(1) From § 2.1, (3) it follows that $a \sqcap a' \leqslant f$.

Thus the law of contradiction holds for this negation, at least in the form that the proposition f which we have designated above as absurd is a consequence of $a \wedge a'$.

The example of Fig. 46 shows that $a \sqcap a' \leqslant f$ can, in fact, occur. Since $f \sqcap a \leqslant f$, it follows from § 2.1 (1a) that:

$$f \leqslant a \sqsubset\!- f = a'.$$

If $f \leqslant a$, then $f \leqslant a \sqcap a'$, hence $a \sqcap a' = f$.

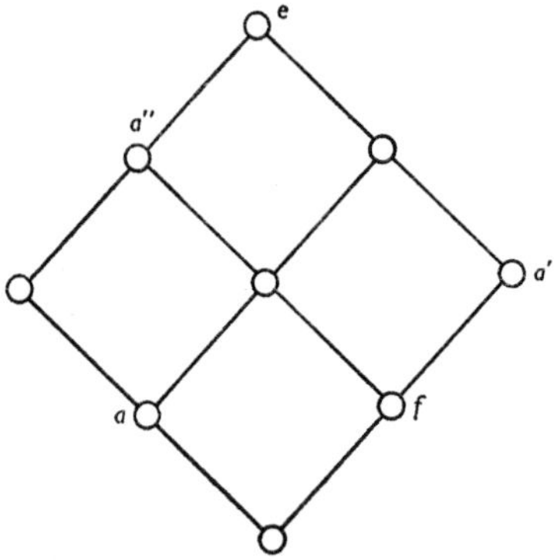

Fig. 46

(2) The law of the excluded middle is expressed by $a \sqcup a' = e$.
The example shows that this does not hold in every subjunctive lattice.

(3) Double negation does not always lead back to a. In our example we have $a < a''$.

Quite generally $a \leqslant a''$; for by definition $a'' = a' \sqsubset\!- f$, i.e. $x \leqslant a'' \leftrightarrow x \sqcap a' \leqslant f$. Since by (1) $a \sqcap a' \leqslant f$, it follows that $a \leqslant a''$.

(4) $$a \leqslant b \rightarrow b' \leqslant a'.$$

Proof. From $a \leqslant b$ it follows that $x \sqcap a \leqslant x \sqcap b$.
From $x \sqcap b \leqslant f$ it follows, therefore, that $x \sqcap a \leqslant f$.

(5) From $a \leqslant a''$ it follows that $a''' \leqslant a'$ (by (4)).

On the other hand, by (3) $a' \leqslant (a')''$.

Hence we have $a''' = a'$. Threefold negation leads back to simple negation.

(6) $$(a \sqcup b)' = a' \sqcap b'.$$

Proof. We use the abbreviation $(a \sqcup b)' = p$.

By (1) we have $\quad p \sqcap (a \sqcup b) \leqslant f,$

i.e. $\quad (p \sqcap a) \sqcup (p \sqcap b) \leqslant f,$

i.e. $\quad p \sqcap a \leqslant f$ and $p \sqcap b \leqslant f,$

this means $p \leqslant a'$ and $p \leqslant b'$, hence $p \leqslant a' \sqcap b'$. On the other hand, if we set $q = a' \sqcap b'$, then going back we find $q \sqcap (a \sqcup b) \leqslant f$, i.e., $q \leqslant (a \sqcup b)'$.

(7) $$a' \sqcup b' \leqslant (a \sqcap b)'.$$

Proof. $\quad a' \sqcup b' \leqslant (a' \sqcup b')''$ by (3),

$\quad = (a'' \sqcap b'')'$ by (6).

Moreover, $\quad a \leqslant a'', b \leqslant b''$ by (3),

hence $\quad a \sqcap b \leqslant a'' \sqcap b'',$

hence $\quad (a'' \sqcap b'')' \leqslant (a \sqcap b)'$ by (4).

That equality does not always hold is shown by the example of Fig. 47. Here we have $a' \sqcup b' = w$, but $(a \sqcap b)' = f' = e$.

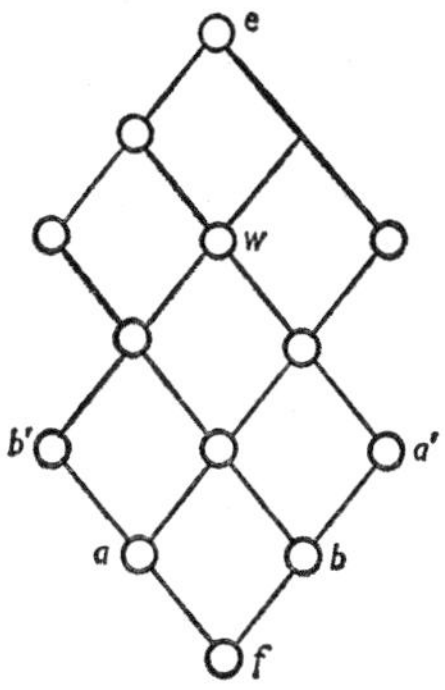

Fig. 47

In the same way one proves in a complete subjunctive lattice, which is then fully distributive, that

(6*) $$\Big(\bigsqcup_{x \in M} x\Big)' = \bigsqcap_{x \in M} x',$$

(7*) $$\bigsqcup_{x \in M} x' \leqslant \Big(\bigsqcap_{x \in M} x\Big)'.$$

One does not obtain further-reaching results by assuming that V contains a null element n and taking $f = n$. Of course, (1) then becomes

$a \sqcap a' = f$, but in the remaining cases of the example we have actually taken $f = n$.

Incidentally, it is always possible to add a null element to a subjunctive lattice V that does not contain one. One chooses as a fundamental set $V^* = V \cup \{n\}$ with an $n \notin V$ and defines: $\bigwedge_{x \in V} n < x$.

The fact that $(V^*, \leqslant)$ is a lattice, is clear. To show that this lattice is subjunctive one has to verify that every set $S_{ab} = \{x; x \sqcap a \leqslant b\}$ has an upper limit belonging to S_{ab}.

1) If a and b both lie in V, then this is clear.

2) If $a = n$, then $x \sqcap n \leqslant b$ holds for all x. S_{ab} contains e as upper limit.

3) If $a \neq n$, hence $a \in V$, and $b = n$, then S_{an} consists only of the element n and this is the upper limit. For if $x \neq n$, then $x \in V$, hence $x \sqcap a \in V$, i.e., $x \sqcap a > n$.

§ 3. Boolean lattices

A Boolean lattice (see page 15 and page 122) is defined as a distributive complemented lattice; thus, it contains n and e and for every element a one and only one element a^0 with

$$a \sqcap a^0 = n, \quad a \sqcup a^0 = e. \tag{1}$$

For a Boolean lattice we use the letter B instead of V.

3.1. Every Boolean lattice is subjunctive

For if we introduce an operation by

$$a \sqsubset b = a^0 \sqcup b,$$

then $a \sqsubset b$ has the property

$$\bigwedge_{x \in B} x \leqslant a \sqsubset b \leftrightarrow x \sqcap a \leqslant b.$$

Proof. 1) From $x \leqslant a^0 \sqcup b$ it follows that

$$x \sqcap a \leqslant (a^0 \sqcup b) \sqcap a = (a^0 \sqcap a) \sqcup (b \sqcap a) = b \sqcap a \leqslant b.$$

2) From $x \sqcap a \leqslant b$ it follows that

$$a^0 \sqcup b \geqslant a^0 \sqcup (x \sqcap a) = (a^0 \sqcup x) \sqcap (a^0 \sqcup a) = a^0 \sqcup x \geqslant x.$$

If we continue to denote the pseudo-complement introduced in the preceding section by $a' = a \sqsubset f$ and set $f = n$, then we obtain

$$a' = a \sqsubset n = a^0 \sqcup n = a^0.$$

So everything proved in the last section for a' also holds for the complement a^0 provided we set $f=n$. But in addition we have $a \sqcup a_0 = e$, i.e., in the logical interpretation the law of the excluded middle. Moreover,

$$a^{00} = a. \tag{2}$$

For a^{00} is defined by $a^0 \sqcap a^{00} = n \wedge a^0 \sqcup a^{00} = e$, and from this and (1) it follows by the cancellation law that $a^{00} = a$.

If we now go through the proof of § 2.2, (7), page 129, then we see that since $a^{00} = a$, the $\leqslant$ symbol can be replaced by the $=$ symbol. Hence we have—we also repeat § 2.2, (6)—

$$(a \sqcup b)^0 = a^0 \sqcap b^0, \tag{3.1}$$

$$(a \sqcap b)^0 = a^0 \sqcup b^0 \tag{3.2}$$

and in complete Boolean lattices

$$\Big(\bigsqcup_{x \in M} x\Big)^0 = \bigsqcap_{x \in M} x^0, \tag{4.1}$$

$$\Big(\bigsqcap_{x \in M} x\Big)^0 = \bigsqcup_{x \in M} x^0. \tag{4.2}$$

These equations bear the name of De Morgan. They can equally well be verified by the means of the definition (1), for example by checking for (3.1) that

$$(a \sqcup b) \sqcap a^0 \sqcap b^0 = n, \quad a \sqcup b \sqcup (a^0 \sqcap b^0) = e.$$

3.2. Examples

1) The collection $\mathfrak{P}e$ of all subsets of a set e forms a complete Boolean lattice with inclusion ($\subseteq$) as the order relation. A good illustration is, for instance, the particular case when e is the set of points in the interior and on the boundary of a rectangle.

$\mathfrak{P}e$ is fully distributive. This can be verified as follows:

$$\xi \in a \sqcap \bigsqcup_M x \text{ means } \xi \in a \wedge \bigvee_{x \in M} \xi \in x,$$

$$\xi \in \bigsqcup_M a \sqcap x \text{ means } \bigvee_{x \in M} (\xi \in a \wedge \xi \in x).$$

With the rule (Q3) of Chapter I, § 1, page 22 we obtain

$$a \sqcap \bigsqcup_M x = \bigsqcup_M a \sqcap x.$$

2) For an example of a subjunctive lattice we choose e as a topological space and $\mathfrak{O}e$ as the totality of open sets. To understand this example the reader is assumed to be familiar with the basic concepts of topology, in particular the concepts 'open set' and 'neighbourhood'. An open set is one that contains with every point a neighbourhood of this point. From this it follows that the empty set $\emptyset = n$ and e are themselves open sets. An abstract characterization of open sets is: the intersection of two (hence finitely many) and the union of arbitrarily many open sets are again open sets; in symbols:

$$a, b \in \mathfrak{O}e \rightarrow a \cap b \in \mathfrak{O}e,$$

$$\bigwedge_{x \in M} (x \in \mathfrak{O}e) \rightarrow \bigsqcup_{x \in M} x \in \mathfrak{O}e.$$

Hence $\mathfrak{O}e$ is a $\sqcup$-complete sublattice of $\mathfrak{P}e$ and so fully distributive by § 1.4.

Let $a^0 \leftrightharpoons \{\xi; \xi \notin a\}$ be the complement of a in $\mathfrak{P}e$, a' the pseud-complement of a in $\mathfrak{O}e$ relative to $f = n$.

In $\mathfrak{P}e$ we have $a \ulcorner\!\!- b = a^0 \cup b$. If a and b are open sets, then a^0 and so $a^0 \cup b$, need not be open sets. But the union of all open sets contained in $a^0 \cup b$ is an open set; we denote it by $i(a^0 \cup b)$ (the set of interior points of $a^0 \cup b$). The reader should check that in $\mathfrak{O}e$

$$a \ulcorner\!\!- b = i(a^0 \cup b).$$

From this it follows that

$$a' = a \ulcorner\!\!- n = i(a^0 \cup n) = i(a^0).$$

3) *Switching algebra.* Certain problems in electrical engineering can be solved by suitable combinations of 'switches'. Here a switch is understood to be part of a circuit between two 'terminals'; all that matters is not the magnitude of the resistance, but whether the switch is open or closed. We assign to a switch the conductor value 0 if it is open, and 1 if it is closed. The value of a switch corresponds to the truth value of a statement. This analogy goes further: if two switches with the values a and b are connected in series, then the value of the circuit between the terminals A and B (Fig. 48) is equal to 1 if and only if $a = 1$ and $b = 1$. If switches with the values a and b are connected in parallel, then the value between A and B is 0 if and only if $a = 0$ and $b = 0$ (Fig. 49).

This corresponds to the truth tables of the connectives $\wedge$ and $\vee$. We shall therefore use these symbols also for combinations of switches and their conductor values.

Fig. 48

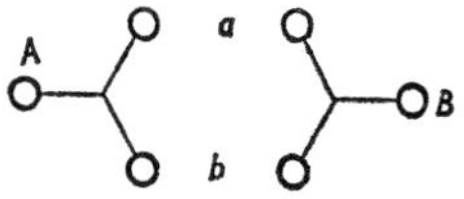

Fig. 49

Two switches in distinct circuits can be coupled by a relay (Fig. 50). It can be arranged that the relay closes the switch b if current is flowing in it; in this case b is called a working contact and the conductor values a and b are equal: $a=b$. But it can also be arranged that the relay opens the switch b; then b is called a rest contact, and we have $b=0$ for $a=1$, and $b=1$ for $a=0$. We write $b=a^0$.

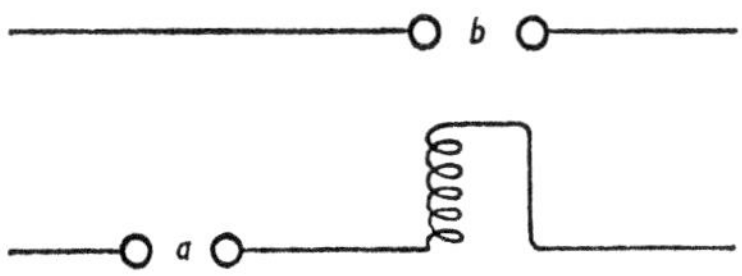

Fig. 50

From the truth tables for $\wedge$, $\vee$ and the complement a^0, all the operational rules of a Boolean lattice can be derived, as we have explained in the introduction.

Here the Boolean lattice consists of the two elements 0 and 1 only, and the variables $a, b \ldots$ assume only these values.

In the algebra of switches one is concerned with networks in which, for instance, between two terminals a number of switches of the values $x_1, x_2, \ldots x_k$ are partly connected in parallel, partly in series, partly coupled by relays. The conducting value between the initial and the final terminal is then a function of $x_1, \ldots x_k$, given by a formula that is formed from $x_1, \ldots x_k$ by means of the operation $\wedge$, $\vee$, ^{0}. We call such a function a *Boolean function*.

One of the tasks of the algebra of switches is to find networks that have prescribed effects. A simple example is the alternating switch: a

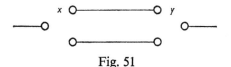

Fig. 51

circuit is to be opened or closed from two places (Fig. 51). This means that a function of two variables x, y is required which changes its value if and only if one of the two variables changes its value, in other words,

$$f(x^0,y) = f(x,y^0) = f^0(x,y).$$

In the next section we shall treat Boolean functions in a slightly more general framework and shall then come back to this problem.

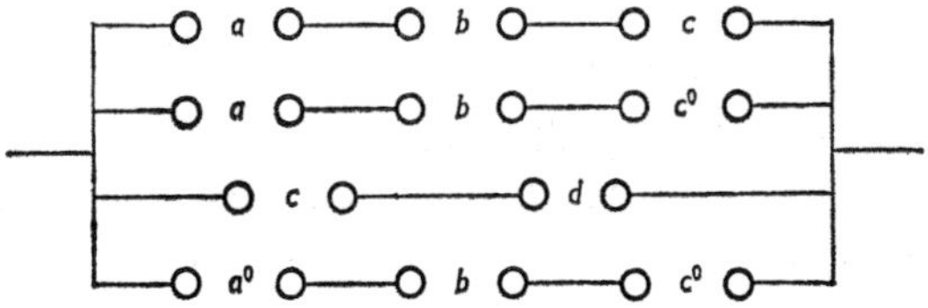

Fig. 52

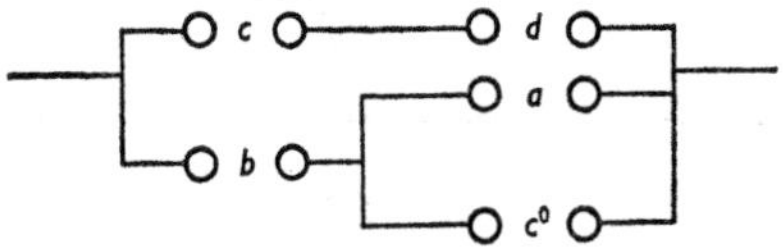

Fig. 53

Another task of switching algebra is the simplification of switches. A fairly trivial example is illustrated by Figs. 52 and 53. We write ab instead of $a \wedge b$. The switch of Fig. 52 is described by

$$abc \vee abc^0 \vee cd \vee a^0bc^0.$$

It simplifies to

$$ab(c \vee c^0) \vee cd \vee a^0bc^0$$

—this could also have been read off the sketch immediately—and since

$$c \vee c^0 = 1,$$

to

$$ab \vee cd \vee a^0bc^0 = cd \vee b(a \vee a^0c^0).$$

Now by the distributive law $a \vee a^0c^0 = (a \vee a^0)(a \vee c^0) = a \vee c^0$. (Fig. 54 illustrates this.) So we obtain for our switchwork

$$cd \vee b(a \vee c^0). \text{ (Fig. 53)}$$

The difficulty of the problem raised here lies partly in the fact that it is hardly possible to state in a unique way how the technologically simplest switchwork is to be characterized. The switchwork with the

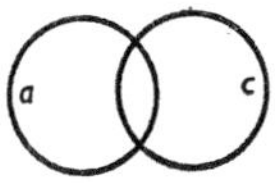

Fig. 54

smallest number of contacts will not always be technologically the best. But even if this criterion is recognized, there is so far no general method known that leads from a given switchwork always to the simplest.

3.3. General aspects of Boolean functions

We start out from a Boolean lattice B in which the null element is denoted by 0, the unit element by 1, the complement of x by x^0, and where we write pq instead of $p \sqcap q$. We define the concept

Boolean formula:

1) Every variable and every constant is a Boolean formula.

2) If p and q are Boolean formulae, then so also are p^0, pq, $p \sqcup q$.

3) All Boolean formulae arise in the given manner.

A *Boolean function* is a mapping of B into itself represented by a Boolean formula. Here we discuss only Boolean functions of two variables (x, y), because the most frequently used notions already occur in this case.

In a Boolean formula it can be arranged by means of De Morgan's formulae (§ 3.1, page 131) that the complement need only be taken of individual variables. In that case each such formula can be represented as an adjunction of conjunctions. A conjunction that also contains together with a variable its complement is 0 and can therefore be omitted in the adjunction. Hence every Boolean formula in two variables can be represented as an adjunction of one or several of the conjunctions 1, x, y, x^0, y^0, xy, xy^0, x^0y, x^0y^0 together with constants.

Since $q = q(y \sqcup y^0) = qy \sqcup qy^0$, by this and similar multiplications it can be arranged that every conjunction contains each variable or its complement.

In general, a Boolean function of two variables can be written as follows:

$$f(x,y) = a_{11}xy \sqcup a_{10}xy^0 \sqcup a_{01}x^0y \sqcup a_{00}x^0y^0. \tag{1}$$

If we set $x=x^1$, then this can be contracted to

$$f(x,y) = \bigsqcup_{i,k=0}^{1} a_{ik}x^iy^k.$$

If B consists of the elements 0, 1 only, as in logic and the algebra of switches, then for k variables there are 2^k constants $a_{i_1 \ldots i_k}$; each can assume the values 0 or 1. Consequently there are $2^{(2^k)}$ Boolean functions of k variables. This number grows very rapidly with k. Therefore, even for rather small values of k it is practically impossible to survey the totality of networks with k switches.

For $k=2$ one obtains 16 functions; $f(x,y)=0$ and $f(x,y)=1$ are, of course, counted among them.

If one sets, for example, $x=0, y=1$ in (1), then

$$x^0y = 1, \quad xy = xy^0 = x^0y^0 = 0.$$

One obtains: $f(0,1)=a_{01}$. Quite generally one finds in this way:

$$f(x,y) = f(1,1)xy \sqcup f(1,0)xy^0 \sqcup f(0,1)x^0y \sqcup f(0,0)x^0y^0 \tag{2}$$

and if i, k, l assume the values 0, 1 for example,

$$f(x,y,z) = \bigsqcup_{i,k,l} f(i,k,l)x^iy^kz^l. \tag{2'}$$

This result was known to Boole. A Boolean function is uniquely determined by its values for the arguments (i,k) or (i,k,l), respectively $(i,k,l=0,1)$.

3.4. *Addition. The Boolean lattice as a ring*

In the problem of the alternating switch we were looking for a function with the property

$$f(x^0,y) = f(x,y^0) = f^0(x,y) \tag{3}$$

If we denote the value of f for the argument $(0,0)$ by $f(0,0)=a$, then it follows from (3) that

$$f(0,1) = f(1,0) = a^0, f(1,1) = a,$$

hence

$$f(x,y) = a(xy \sqcup x^0y^0) \sqcup a^0(xy^0 \sqcup x^0y). \tag{4}$$

One readily verifies that (4) satisfies conditions (3) for every value of a. (The equation

$$(xy^0 \sqcup x^0y)^0 = xy \sqcup x^0y^0 \tag{5}$$

is useful in making the calculations.)

In the algebra of switches a can only assume the values 0 or 1. So one obtains two solutions of the problem:

$$f_1(x,y) = xy^0 \sqcup x^0y, \tag{6a}$$

$$f_2(x,y) = xy \sqcup x^0y^0. \tag{6b}$$

An inspection of Fig. 55 shows that they are equivalent from the point of view of electrical engineering.

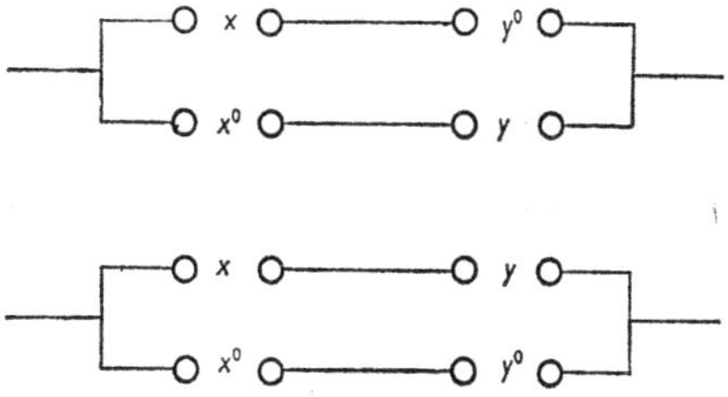

Fig. 55

The function f_1 also occurs in the problem of binary addition. If two numbers are given in the binary system by sequences of 0's and 1's, then a calculating machine adding the digits x and y must yield the sum and transfer digit according to the following table. The table of values for the sum is precisely that of the function $f_1(x,y)$, the table

x	0	0	1	1
y	0	1	0	1
Sum	0	1	1	0
Transfer	0	0	0	1

for the transfer digit is that of the function $f(x,y) = xy$. A technical realization by means of relays is represented diagrammatically in Fig. 56. In practice such switching functions are realized by diodes and other means.

In the logical interpretation the function f_1 signifies that either x is true but not y, or that y is true but not x, i.e., we have the propositional connective by the exclusive 'either–or'.

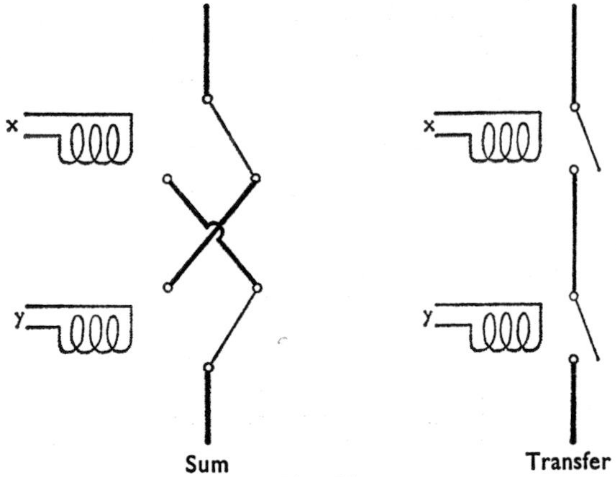

Fig. 56

If the relays x, y are not in operation, then the opposite switches are in the position indicated. If, for example, the relay x on the left is in operation but not y, then the switch at x is changed and the part of the circuit denoted by 'sum' carries current.

In set theory $x \cap y^0$ is called the *difference* of x and y (see Fig. 57).

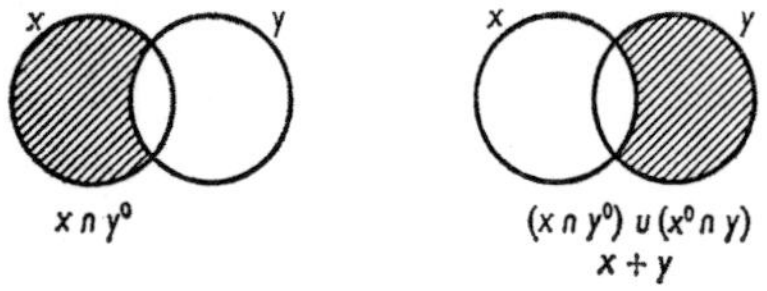

Fig. 57

$$(x \cap y^0) \cup (x^0 \cap y) = f_1(x,y)$$

is called *symmetric difference* or *sum mod* 2. One of the most important theorems on Boolean lattices is as follows: If in B an addition is defined by

(7) $$x+y \leftrightharpoons xy^0 \sqcup x^0y$$

and a multiplication by

(8) $$x \cdot y \leftrightharpoons x \sqcap y$$

(that is the reason why we have written xy), then $(B, +, \cdot)$ is a commutative ring. The neutral element for addition is 0 (i.e., the null element of B), the neutral element for multiplication is 1 (the unit element of B). For every element we have $xx = x$ and $x + x = 0$.

For the *proof* we have to verify the axioms of a commutative ring.

$$xy = yx$$
$$(xy)z = x(yz), \quad xx = x$$
$$1 \cdot x = x \cdot 1 = x$$

are already known to us,

$x + y = y + x$ follows immediately from (7).

$x + (y + z) = (x + y) + z$

and $x(y + z) = xy + xz$ are easily checked.

Next, an immediate consequence of (7) is

$$x + 0 = x$$

and

(9) $$x + x = 0.$$

0 is the null element for addition, and for every x there is an element $-x$ with $x + (-x) = 0$, namely $-x = x$. So we have no need for the symbol '$-$'.

The lattice operations are expressed in terms of the ring operations as follows:

1) From (7) it follows that

(10) $$x + 1 = x^0$$

2) If $xy = 0$, then $xy^0 = x(y+1) = x$,

$$x^0 y = (x+1)y = y,$$

hence

(11) $$xy = 0 \qquad x + y = x \sqcup y.$$

Now we have quite generally

$$\begin{aligned} (x+y)xy &= xy + xy = 0, \\ x + y + xy &= (x+y) \sqcup xy \\ &= xy^0 \sqcup x^0 y \sqcup xy (\sqcup yx) \\ &= x(y^0 \sqcup y) \sqcup y(x^0 \sqcup x) \end{aligned}$$

(12) $$x + y + xy = x \sqcup y.$$

Definition. A ring $(B, +, \cdot)$ with unit element in which every element is idempotent, i.e., $xx = x$, is called *Boolean ring*.

Theorem. If one defines in a Boolean ring $(B, +, \cdot)$

$$\begin{aligned} x \sqcap y &= x \cdot y, \\ x \sqcup y &= x + y + xy, \\ x^0 &= x + 1, \end{aligned}$$

then $(B, \sqcap, \sqcup, {}^0)$ is a Boolean lattice.

Proof.

1) $$xy = yx.$$

For since every element is idempotent,

$$\begin{aligned} x+y = (x+y)(x+y &= xx+xy+yx+yy \\ &= x+y+xy+yx, \end{aligned}$$

hence

(13) $$xy+yx = 0.$$

This holds for every x and every y, in particular for $y = x$:

(14) $$x+x = 0.$$

If we write here xy instead of x, we obtain

(15) $$xy+xy = 0.$$

A comparison of (13) and (15) shows that $xy = yx$.

2) $x \sqcup y = y \sqcup x$ follows immediately from the definition.

3) The associative, distributive, and absorption laws can be checked by computation.

4) The null element of the ring (the neutral element of addition) has the properties $x \cdot 0 = 0$, hence $x \sqcap 0 = 0$, i.e., $0 \leqslant x$ for all x. The unit element of the ring (the neutral element of multiplication) has the property $x \cdot 1 = x$, i.e., $x \leqslant 1$ for all x.

5) For $x^0 = x + 1$ we have

$$\begin{aligned} xx^0 &= xx + x = x + x = 0; \\ x \sqcup x^0 &= x + x^0 + xx^0 = x + x + 1 = 1. \end{aligned}$$

Some computations in Boolean lattices, in particular the investigation of Boolean functions, are simplified by the use of addition.

$x^i y^k x^j y^l$ is $\neq 0$ if and only if $i=j$ and $k=l$. Any two conjunctions of the form (1) therefore have the intersection 0; hence by (11) $f(x,y)=a_{11}xy+a_{10}xy^0+a_{01}xy^0+a_{00}x^0y^0$. If we substitute $x^0=x+1$, $y^0=y+1$, then we obtain for f the additive normal form

(16) $$f(x,y) = a+bx+cx+dxy.$$

Here

$$a = a_{00}$$
$$b = a_{10}+a_{00}$$
$$c = a_{01}+a_{00}$$
$$d = a_{11}+a_{10}+a_{01}+a_{00}.$$

The conditions for the alternating switch now assume the form

$$f(x,y+1) = f(x+1,y) = f(x,y)+1;$$

one sees immediately that they are satisfied by

$$f(x,y) = a+x+y$$

for arbitrary a. For $a=0$ we obtain f_1, for $a=1$ we obtain f_2.

3.5. Functions of a single variable

The adjunctive normal form of a function $f(x)$ is

(1) $$f(x) = px \sqcup qx^0,$$

the additive normal form is

(2) $$f(x) = a+bx.$$

Here $a=q$, $b=p+q$.

3.5.1. Our first question concerns the zeros of $f(x)$, i.e., the solution of the equation

(3) $$bx = a.$$

Since $bx \leqslant b$, it is soluble only if

$$a \leqslant b.$$

But then $x=a$ is a solution.

All solution of (3) can be found by a method well known for linear equations: if x, y are two solutions of (3), then

$$b(x+y) = 0.$$

Thus, $x+y$ is a solution of the associated homogeneous equation

$$bz = 0 \tag{4}$$

and one obtains all solutions of (3) by adding all solutions of (4) to one solution of (3)—in our case $x=a$.

But now (4) is equivalent to

$$b^0 z = (b+1)z = z,$$

hence to $z \leqslant b^0$.

Therefore, all solutions of $bx=a$, with $a \leqslant b$, are

$$x = a+z,\ z \leqslant b^0. \tag{5}$$

Thus the solution is unique if and only if $b^0=0$, that is, if (3) has the form

$$x = a.$$

The mapping $x \rightarrowtail y=a+bx$ is uniquely invertible if and only if $b=1$.

3.5.2. *What are the values that $f(x)$ can assume?* We shall use form (1), because we have to work with the order relation and this is compatible with $\sqcap$, $\sqcup$, but not with $+$; in other words, the statement 'if $a \leqslant b$, then $a+c \leqslant b+c$' is not true for all c, for example for $c=1$. We have

$$pqx \leqslant px \leqslant p,$$
$$pqx^0 \leqslant qx^0 \leqslant q.$$

Adjunction yields

$$pq \leqslant px \sqcup qx^0 = f(x) \leqslant p \sqcup q. \tag{6}$$

These bounds are in fact attained:

$$f(p) = p \sqcup q, \quad f(q) = pq.$$

We claim that the function attains every intermediate value, i.e., the equation

$$px \sqcup qx^0 = w \tag{7}$$

is always soluble if

$$pq \leqslant w \leqslant p \sqcup q \tag{8}$$

To prove this we go over to the additive form. Since $pxqx^0=0$, we have $px \sqcup qx^0 = px+qx^0$. (7) becomes

$$(p+q)x = q+w. \tag{9}$$

By *3.5.1.* this equation is soluble if and only if

$$q+w \leqslant p+q, \text{ i.e. } (q+w)(p+q) = q+w,$$

(10) $$pq+w(p+q) = w.$$

Now (8) states that

$$w(p \sqcup q) = w(p+q+pq) = w,$$
$$wpq = pq.$$

Formula (10) follows from these two equations. Thus, $f(x)=px \sqcup qx^0$ maps B onto the sublattice $f(B)=p \sqcup q/pq$.

3.5.3. *Rules of calculation*

If $$f(x) = px+qx^0 = (p+q)x+q,$$

then

$$f^0(x) = (p+q)x+q+1 = (p+1+q+1)x+q+1$$
$$= (p^0+q^0)x+q^0.$$

If $$f_1(x) = p_1x \sqcup q_1x^0 = p_1x+q_1x^0,$$
$$f_2(x) = p_2x \sqcup q_2x^0 = p_2x+q_2x^0,$$

then

$$f_1(x)\cdot f_2(x) = p_1p_2x+q_1q_2x^0,$$
$$f_1(x)+f_2(x) = (p_1+p_2)x+(q_1+q_2)x^0,$$
$$f_1(x) \sqcup f_2(x) = (p_1 \sqcup p_2)x+(q_1 \sqcup q_2)x^0.$$

3.5.4. *Functions with special properties*

1. *When is f a monotone function?*

It is postulated that

$$x \leqslant y \rightarrow f(x) \leqslant f(y).$$

From this there follows as a necessary condition $f(0) \leqslant f(1)$, i.e., $q \leqslant p$. But this condition is also sufficient; for when $pq=q$, then $f(x)=px \sqcup pqx^0=p(x \sqcup qx^0)=p(x \sqcup q)(x \sqcup x^0)=p(x \sqcup q)$,

(1) $$f(x) = px \sqcup q.$$

This function is monotone because

$$x \leqslant y \rightarrow px \leqslant py \rightarrow px \sqcup q \leqslant py \sqcup q.$$

2. *When is f a homomorphism with respect to multiplication?*

We postulate

$$f(xy) = f(x)\cdot f(y).$$

For $x=1, y=0$ this yields as a necessary condition:

$$f(0) = f(1)\cdot f(0), \text{ i.e. } q = pq.$$

Hence $f(x)=px \sqcup q$ and so

$$\begin{aligned} f(x)\cdot f(y) &= (px \sqcup q)(py \sqcup q) = pxy \sqcup qx \sqcup qy \sqcup q \\ &= pxy \sqcup q = f(xy). \end{aligned}$$

3. *When is f a homomorphism with respect to union?*

It is postulated that

$$f(x \sqcup y) = f(x) \sqcup f(y).$$

$x=1$, $y=0$ yields as a necessary condition $p=p \sqcup q$, hence $q \leqslant p$. By (1) we have

$$f(x) \sqcup f(y) = px \sqcup q \sqcup py \sqcup q = p(x \sqcup y) \sqcup q = f(x \sqcup y).$$

So the conditions 1., 2., 3. are all equivalent to $q \leqslant p$.

4. The mappings of the form $f(x)=px \sqcup q$ with $q \leqslant p$ are, then, lattice endomorphisms of B. Such an endomorphism can only be an automorphism if $f(B)=B$. However, $f(B)=p \sqcup q/pq$, in our case p/q. This is $=B$ only when $p=1, q=0$.

The only lattice automorphism of B induced by a Boolean function is the identity.

Of course, this does not mean that a Boolean lattice B admits no lattice automorphism other than the identity. For example, if B is of finite length, then every element has a unique representation as a union of finitely many atoms. Every permutation of the points induces a lattice automorphism, and these are all the automorphisms, because every automorphism must carry points into points. One can easily check that a mapping $x \to px \sqcup qx^0$ does not, in general, carry points into points.

5. *When is f a homomorphism with respect to addition?*

It is postulated that

$$f(x+y) = f(x)+f(y).$$

For $y=0$ this yields as a necessary condition $f(0)=q=0$. This condition is also sufficient: $f(x)=px$ is a homomorphism relative to addition.

2. and 5. characterize a *ring homomorphism*. Since $q=0$ implies $q \leqslant p$, we have:

Every ring endomorphism of B induced by a Boolean function is a lattice endomorphism, but not every lattice endomorphism is a ring endomorphism.

Example. $f(x)=x \sqcup q$, provided B contains an element q with $0<q<1$.

The clause 'induced by a Boolean function' is superfluous. For if φ is a ring endomorphism, so that

$$\varphi(xy) = \varphi x \cdot \varphi y, \quad \varphi(x+y) = \varphi x + \varphi y,$$

then

$$\varphi(x \sqcup y) = \varphi(x+y+xy) = \varphi x + \varphi y + \varphi x \cdot \varphi y = \varphi x \sqcup \varphi y.$$

3.6. Functions of two variables

3.6.1. Domain of values

Let $$f(x,y) = (px \sqcup qx^0)y \sqcup (rx \sqcup sx^0)y^0.$$

For f as a function of y we have by (6), page 142:

(1) $$(px \sqcup qx^0)(rx \sqcup sx^0) \leqslant f(x,y) \leqslant px \sqcup qx^0 \sqcup rx \sqcup sx^0.$$

Here the lower bound is attained for $y=rx \sqcup sx^0$, the upper for $y=px \sqcup qx^0$.

Expansion of the left-hand side of (1) yields

$$prx \sqcup qsx^0 \leqslant f(x,y) \leqslant (p \sqcup r)x \sqcup (q \sqcup s)x^0.$$

But now, again by page 142,

$$prqs \leqslant prx \sqcup qsx^0,$$

and the lower bound is attained for $x=qs$.

Furthermore, $(p \sqcup r)x \sqcup (q \sqcup s)x^0 \leqslant p \sqcup r \sqcup q \sqcup s,$

and the upper bound is attained for $x = p \sqcup r$.
Altogether we obtain

$$prqs \leqslant f(x,y) \leqslant p \sqcup r \sqcup q \sqcup s,$$

and the lower bound is attained for

$$x = qs, y = rx \sqcup sx^0 = rqs \sqcup s(q^0 \sqcup s^0) = s(r \sqcup q^0);$$

the upper bound is attained for

$$x = p \sqcup r, y = px \sqcup qx^0 = p(p \sqcup r) \sqcup qp^0r^0 = p \sqcup qr^0.$$

3.6.2. Do there exist, apart from the functions discussed in § 3.4, other functions

$$f(x,y) \leftrightharpoons x \top y, \quad g(x,y) \leftrightharpoons x \circ y,$$

such that $(B, \top, \circ)$ is a ring? It is easily seen that the functions

$$f(x,y) = (x+y)^0 = xy \sqcup x^0y^0, \quad g(x,y) = x \sqcup y$$

satisfy the requirements. But are they the only ones?

We begin with a postulate that restricts the class of admissible functions drastically. Trial and error show that unique invertibility of addition is a suitable restriction. So we ask for a function

$$f(x,y) = a+bx+cy+dxy$$

with the property that for every x and every z the equation

$$(a+bx)+(c+dx)y = z$$

has precisely one solution y. By § 3.5.1 (page 142) this is so if and only if

$$c+dx = 1$$

for every x. Substitution of $x=0$ yields $c=1$, of $x=1$ yields $d=0$ as necessary conditions. Evidently together they are also sufficient.

Thus, the required function must have the form

$$f(x,y) = a+bx+y.$$

If we postulate in addition that $a+bx+y=z$ is uniquely soluble in x for all y, z, then we obtain $b=1$, hence

(1) $$f(x,y) = a+x+y.$$

So we see that this connective is commutative, and it is easily checked that it is associative.

It is, then, suitable as an 'addition'. The neutral element is a:

$$f(x,a) = a+x+a = x.$$

If we postulate that the neutral element is to be the null element 0 of the lattice B, then we obtain $f(x,y)=x+y$. If we postulate that 1 is the neutral element, then we obtain $f(x,y)=(x+y)^0$. But first we keep to the general form (1) and ask whether for our f there is a second function

(2) $$g(x,y) = p+qx+ry+sxy \leftrightharpoons x \circ y$$

such that the distributive laws hold:

(3) $$x \circ (y \top z) = x \circ y \top x \circ z,$$

(4) $$(x \top y) \circ z = x \circ z \top y \circ z.$$

By (1) and (2) we have

$$x \circ (y \top z) = p+qx+r(a+y+z)+sx(a+y+z),$$

$$x \circ y \top x \circ z = a+p+qx+ry+sxy+p+qx+rz+sxz.$$

A comparison shows that (3) is satisfied precisely if

$$p+qx+ra+sxa = a.$$

This holds for all x if and only if

(5) $$p+ra = a, \quad q+sa = 0.$$

Similarly (4) holds if and only if

(6) $$p+qa = a, \quad r+sa = 0.$$

From (5) and (6) it follows that

$$q = r = sa, \quad p = a+qa = a+sa,$$

hence

(7) $$x \circ y = a+sa(1+x+y)+sxy.$$

One sees immediately that this multiplication is commutative and one can easily check that it is associative. Thus, with the operation (1) and (7) B forms a ring.

When does there exist a *neutral element of multiplication*? We are looking for a y such that the equation

(8) $$x \circ y = a+sa(1+x)+s(a+x)y = x$$

holds for all x.

For (8) to hold with $x=0$, we must have

(9) $$a+sa+say = 0.$$

Multiplication by s^0 yields

(10) $$as^0 = 0, \text{ i.e., } a(s+1) = 0, \text{ hence } as = a,$$

so that (9) becomes

$$ay = 0.$$

For (8) to hold with $x=1$, we must have

(11) $$a+s(a+1)y = 1.$$

Multiplication by s^0 yields

$$as^0 = s^0.$$

A comparison with (10) shows that

$$s^0 = 0, \text{ hence } s = 1.$$

If we substitute this and $ay=0$ in (11), we obtain

$$a = y = 1, \quad y = a^0.$$

It can be checked that for $s=1$ and $y=a^0$ (8) does, in fact, hold for all x. So we have proved: *The multiplication defined by* (7) *has a neutral element if and only if* $s=1$. *The neutral element is then* a^0. For $s=1$ (7) becomes

(12) $$x \circ y = a(x+y)+xy = ax+(a+x)y.$$

Finally we ask when multiplication is uniquely invertible.

First of all, $a \circ y=a$ for every y, hence the equation $a \circ y=z$ has no solution for $z \neq a$, and for $z=a$ all elements of B are solutions. So we ask when the equation

$$x \circ y = ax+(a+x)y = z$$

is uniquely soluble in y for $x \neq a$ and arbitrary z.

By page 142 this is the case precisely if $a+x=1$, hence $x=a^0$.

If x can assume values other than a and a^0, i.e., if B consists of more than two elements, then multiplication is not uniquely invertible. B can only be a field if it consists of the two elements 0 and 1.

It is easy to verify that B is then, in fact, a field: this is so both for $a=0$, hence $x \top y=x+y$, $x \circ y=xy$, as well as for $a=1$; $x \top y=(x+y)^0$; $x \circ y=x+x^0y=x \sqcup y$.

CHAPTER VII

Decomposition and Embedding Theorems

§ 1. Decomposition of an element into irreducible elements

1.1. Definition. Statement of the problem

The set of natural numbers with divisibility as the order relation forms a distributive lattice (Chapter VI, § 1.2). Every natural number can be represented uniquely as a product of prime numbers. A similar theorem, which easily translates into a theorem of lattice theory, is the following: every natural number can be represented uniquely as the least common multiple (*l.c.m.*, $\sqcup$) of prime powers. Prime powers can be characterized by the fact that they cannot be represented as $\sqcup$ of other natural numbers.

The question arises under what conditions every element of a lattice can be represented as a $\sqcup$ of $\sqcup$-irreducible elements and under what conditions such a representation is unique.

Definition 1. An element p of a lattice $(V, \sqcap, \sqcup)$ is said to be $\sqcup$-*irreducible* or briefly *irreducible* if

(1) $$\bigwedge_x \bigwedge_y (p = x \sqcup y \rightarrow p = x \vee p = y).$$

An element p of a complete lattice is said to be *completely irreducible* if for every subset W of V

(1v) $$p = \bigsqcup_{x \in W} x \rightarrow \bigvee_{x \in W} p = x.$$

Evidently every completely irreducible element is irreducible. The converse does not hold (see Example 2).

Example 1. In every linearly ordered set every element is irreducible.

Example 2. The set of real numbers x with $0 \leqslant_z x \leqslant_z 1$ forms a complete lattice under the order relation $\underset{z}{\leqslant}$. Since it is linearly ordered, every element is irreducible. But none except 0 is completely irreducible, for every element $x \neq 0$ can be represented as the upper limit of elements $\neq x$, for example

$$x = \bigsqcup_k (x - 1/k),$$

where k ranges over the natural numbers $> 1/x$.

Example 3. Let V consist of the pairs (x_1, x_2) of rational numbers with $0 \underset{z}{\leqslant} x_i \underset{z}{\leqslant} 1$. By

$$(x_1, x_2) \leqslant (y_1, y_2) \Leftrightarrow x_1 \underset{z}{\leqslant} y_1 \wedge x_2 \underset{z}{\leqslant} y_2$$

an order relation is defined that makes V into a lattice. (V is the direct product of the linearly ordered sets $M_i = \{x_i;\ 0 \underset{z}{<} x_i \underset{z}{\leqslant} 1\}$.) For every pair (x_1, x_2) there are pairs (y_1, y_2) with $y_1 \underset{z}{<} x_1$, $y_2 \underset{z}{<} x_2$, and we have

$$(x_1, x_2) = (x_1, y_2) \sqcup (y_1, x_2).$$

Hence in this lattice there is no irreducible element whatsoever.

Theorem 1. If V is of finite length below, then every element of V can be represented as a $\sqcup$ of finitely many irreducible elements; we shall say: it can be decomposed into finitely many irreducible elements.

Proof. If a is an irreducible element, we shall of course regard this as a decomposition. Otherwise there exist a_1, a_2 with $a = a_1 \sqcup a_2$; $a_1 < a$, $a_2 < a$. If a_1 and a_2 can be represented as a $\sqcup$ of finitely many irreducible elements, then so can a. If a has no such decomposition, neither has one of a_1 or a_2. The same argument would apply to this element, and so on. So we would obtain a descending infinite chain, and by assumption such a chain does not exist.

That the condition 'of finite length below' is not necessary can be seen in the example of suitable infinite linearly ordered sets. Example 3 can be modified by taking $M_i = \{x_i;\ 0 \underset{z}{\leqslant} x_i \underset{z}{\leqslant} 1\}$. Then the elements $(x_1, 0)$ and $(0, x_2)$ are irreducible, and every element of V is representable as $(x_1, x_2) = (x_1, 0) \sqcup (0, x_2)$.

For recent investigations on this and related problems see R. P. Dilworth, 'Structure and decomposition theory of lattices', *Proceedings of Symposia in Pure Mathematics II, Lattice Theory*. or, Amer. Math. Soc. 1961.

1.2. Uniqueness of the decomposition in distributive lattices

Example 1. ($\bar{d}$) see Fig. 41, page 118. The elements n, a, b, c, are irreducible.

$$e = a \sqcup b = b \sqcup c = c \sqcup a = a \sqcup b \sqcup c.$$

Example 2. ($\bar{m}$) see Fig. 22, 1, page 76. The elements n, a, b, c, are irreducible.

$$e = a \sqcup b = c \sqcup b.$$

Example 3. The lattice of divisors of 12, see Fig. 16, page 63.

$$12 = 4 \sqcup 3 = 2 \sqcup 4 \sqcup 3.$$

In the first and third examples we meet 'redundant' decompositions, which have to be excluded in discussing uniqueness.

Definition 2. A decomposition $a = \bigsqcup_N p$ is called *irredundant* if for every p_0 in N we have $\bigsqcup_{N-p_0} p < a$.

($N - p_0$ is the set arising from N by omission of p_0.)

If $\bigsqcup_{N-p_0} p = a$, then p_0 is said to be *superfluous*.

The examples 1 and 2 show that we cannot expect a uniqueness theorem in a non-distributive lattice.

Theorem 2. If in a distributive lattice an element a has an irredundant decomposition into irreducible elements, then this decomposition is unique.

Preliminary remark. The uniqueness of the decomposition of the natural number into prime factors is due to the following fact, valid for every prime: if p divides a product, then p divides at least one of the factors. However, the following related result is more suitable for translation into lattice theory: if p divides the l.c.m. $a \sqcup b$, then p also divides one of the numbers a or b. More generally, we prove

Lemma 1. In a distributive lattice, if p is irreducible and $p \leqslant a \sqcup b$, then $p \leqslant a$ or $p \leqslant b$.

Proof. $p \leqslant a \sqcup b$ implies $p = p \sqcap (a \sqcup b) = (p \sqcap a) \sqcup (p \sqcap b)$. Since p is irreducible, it follows that $p = p \sqcap a$ or $p = p \sqcap b$, i.e., $p \leqslant a$ or $p \leqslant b$.

A consequence of this lemma is: if in a decomposition

$$a = p_1 \sqcup p_2 \sqcup \ldots \sqcup p_k$$

one of the p_i is superfluous, then not only is

$$p_i \leqslant p_1 \sqcup \ldots \sqcup p_{i-1} \sqcup p_{i+1} \sqcup \ldots \sqcup p_k,$$

but there is a $j \neq i$ with $p_i \leqslant p_j$. We then say that the decomposition of a is *directly redundant*. Thus, what we have just proved may be expressed by saying: in a distributive lattice every redundant decomposition is directly redundant.

If now $$a = p_1 \sqcup \ldots \sqcup p_k = q_1 \sqcup \ldots \sqcup q_l$$

are two irredundant decompositions of a into irreducible elements, then for every p_i there is a q_m with $p_i \leqslant q_m$ and for q_m again a p_j with $q_m \leqslant p_j$. Hence $p_i \leqslant q_m \leqslant p_j$. Since no p_i is superfluous, it follows that $i=j$, hence $p_i = q_m$. Thus, Theorem 2 is proved.

In the same way one proves: if V is complete and fully distributive (see Chapter VI, § 1.4, page 122), then every element of V has at most one decomposition into completely irreducible elements.

Converse. If in a lattice V every element has one and only one directly irredundant decomposition into finitely many irreducible elements, then V is distributive.

Lemma 2. Under the conditions stated we have: if p is irreducible and $p \leqslant a \sqcup b$, then $p \leqslant a$ or $p \leqslant b$.

Proof. If $a = q_1 \sqcup \ldots \sqcup q_k$, $b = r_1 \sqcup \ldots \sqcup r_l$ are the decompositions of a and b, then

$$a \sqcup b = q_1 \sqcup \ldots \sqcup q_k \sqcup r_1 \sqcup \ldots \sqcup r_l,$$

after omission of superfluous elements, is the unique directly irredundant decomposition of $a \sqcup b$. From $p \leqslant a \sqcup b$ it follows that

$$a \sqcup b = p \sqcup a \sqcup b = p \sqcup q_1 \sqcup \ldots \sqcup r_l$$

(where in $q_1 \sqcup \ldots \sqcup r_l$ the superfluous elements have been deleted) and this is not a second decomposition of $a \sqcup b$ only when p is superfluous, i.e. $p \leqslant$ a q_i or $\leqslant$ an r_j.

To prove distributivity we have to show that

$$a \sqcap (b \sqcup c) \leqslant (a \sqcap b) \sqcup (a \sqcap c).$$

If $a \sqcap (b \sqcup c) = p_1 \sqcup \ldots \sqcup p_k$, then for each of these p

$$p \leqslant a \wedge p \leqslant b \sqcup c,$$

i.e. by the lemma

$$p \leqslant a \wedge (p \leqslant b \vee p \leqslant c),$$

and by the distributivity of propositional connectives

$$(p \leqslant a \wedge p \leqslant b) \vee (p \leqslant a \wedge p \leqslant c),$$

whence
$$p \leqslant a \sqcap b \vee p \leqslant a \sqcap c,$$

and so
$$p \leqslant (a \sqcap b) \sqcup (a \sqcap c).$$

1.3. The exchange theorem in modular lattices

Theorem 3. If V is modular and if

(1) $$a = p_1 \sqcup \ldots \sqcup p_k = q_1 \sqcup \ldots \sqcup q_l$$

are two irredundant decompositions of a into irreducible elements, then for every p_i there is a q_j such that

(2) $$a = p_1 \sqcup \ldots \sqcup p_{i-1} \sqcup q_j \sqcup p_{i+1} \sqcup \ldots \sqcup p_k.$$

Before the proof we give an example and a preliminary discussion.

Example. A special case of the theorem is well known in vector space theory. If $\mathfrak{V}$ is a vector space of finite dimension k over a field S (elements of $\mathfrak{V}$ are denoted by small gothic letters, elements of S by small Greek letters), then there exist k basis vectors $\mathfrak{e}_1, \ldots, \mathfrak{e}_k$ so that every element of $\mathfrak{V}$ can be written uniquely in the form

(3) $$\mathfrak{x} = \mathfrak{e}_1\xi_1 + \ldots + \mathfrak{e}_k\xi_k$$

The basis vectors are not uniquely determined. But if $\mathfrak{n}'_1, \ldots, \mathfrak{n}'_l$ is another basis, then $l = k$ and for every $\mathfrak{e}_i$ there is an $\mathfrak{n}'_j$ with the property that $\mathfrak{e}_1, \ldots \mathfrak{e}_{i-1}, \mathfrak{n}'_j, \mathfrak{e}_{i+1}, \ldots, \mathfrak{e}_k$ is a basis (Exchange Theorem of Grassmann and Steinitz). To obtain the lattice-theoretical formulation we observe that the subsets

$$\mathfrak{E}_i = \{e_i\xi;\ \xi \in S\}$$

of $\mathfrak{V}$ are subspaces and that for two subspaces $\mathfrak{A}$ and $\mathfrak{B}$ of $\mathfrak{V}$:

$$\mathfrak{A} \sqcup \mathfrak{B} = \{\mathfrak{a} + \mathfrak{b};\ \mathfrak{a} \in \mathfrak{A}, \mathfrak{b} \in \mathfrak{B}\}.$$

(3) then translates into a representation of $\mathfrak{V}$:

$$\mathfrak{V} = \mathfrak{E}_1 \sqcup \ldots \sqcup \mathfrak{E}_k.$$

Similar basis representations exist for all subspaces of $\mathfrak{V}$.

Preliminary discussion. Let $a = p \sqcup p^* = q \sqcup q^*$ and $p \sqcap p^* = q \sqcup q^* = = q \sqcap p^* = p \sqcap q^* = n$. (See Fig. 58.) To exchange p with q we consider the mapping: $x \rightarrowtail \varphi x = p^* \sqcup x$. φ is an isomorphism of p/n onto a/p^* (see Chapter V, § 3, page 80), and if $a = q \sqcup p^*$—as we shall prove later—also an isomorphism of q/n onto a/p^* that carries q into a. The mapping $y \rightarrowtail \psi y = p \sqcap y$ is an isomorphism of a/p^* onto p/n that carries a into p. By performing the two mappings in succession q is carried into p.

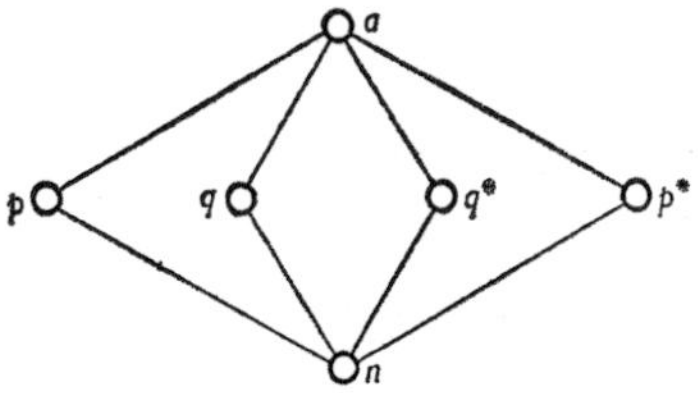

Fig. 58

These preliminary remarks are meant to motivate the use of the next lemma, which can be stated as follows: the mapping $\psi\varphi$ is a $\sqcup$-homomorphism for all $x, y \leqslant p \sqcup p^*$.

Lemma. In a modular lattice for all $x, y \leqslant p \sqcup p^*$ we have

$$[p \sqcap (p^* \sqcup x)] \sqcup [p \sqcap (p^* \sqcup y)] = p \sqcap (p^* \sqcup x \sqcup y).$$

Proof. We note once more the modular law:

(m) $$w \leqslant u \rightarrow u \sqcap (v \sqcup w) = (u \sqcap v) \sqcup w.$$

With $u = p$, $v = p^* \sqcup x$, $w = p \sqcap (p^* \sqcup y)$ this yields

$$[p \sqcap (p^* \sqcup x)] \sqcup [p \sqcap (p^* \sqcup y)] = p \sqcap [p^* \sqcup x \sqcup (p \sqcap (p^* \sqcup y))],$$

and the assertion reduces to

$$p^* \sqcup (p \sqcap (p^* \sqcup y)) = p^* \sqcup y.$$

Now (m) with $u = p^* \sqcup y$, $v = p$, $w = p^*$ yields

$$p^* \sqcup (p \sqcap (p^* \sqcup y)) = (p^* \sqcup y) \sqcap (p^* \sqcup p),$$

and if $y \leqslant p \sqcup p^*$, then $p^* \sqcup y \leqslant p^* \sqcup p$,

hence $(p^* \sqcup y) \sqcap (p^* \sqcup p) = p^* \sqcup y$.

This proves the lemma.

For the proof of the exchange theorem we set

$$p_i = p, p_1 \sqcup \ldots \sqcup p_{i-1} \sqcup p_{i+1} \sqcup \ldots \sqcup p_k = p^*.$$

From the lemma it follows that:

$$[p \sqcap (p^* \sqcup q_1)] \sqcup [p \sqcap (p^* \sqcup q_2)] \sqcup \ldots \sqcup [p^* \sqcap (p^* \sqcup q_l)] = \\ p \sqcap (p^* \sqcup a) = p \sqcap a = p.$$

Since p is irreducible, there exists a j for which

$$p = p \sqcap (p^* \sqcup q_j), \text{ i.e. } p \leqslant p^* \sqcup q_j$$

Hence $a = p \sqcup p^* \leqslant p^* \sqcup q_j$.

On the other hand, $p^* \leqslant a$ and $q_j \leqslant a$, hence $p^* \sqcup q_j \leqslant a$. And so $a = p^* \sqcup q_j$, as required.

In the non-modular lattice $(\bar{m})$, Fig. 22. 1, page 76, the exchange theorem is valid, but not, for example, in the lattice with the order diagram of Fig. 59. Here

$$a = p \sqcup p^* = q \sqcup q^*$$

but

$$p \sqcup q < a, p \sqcup q^* < a, p^* \sqcup q < a, p^* \sqcup q^* < a.$$

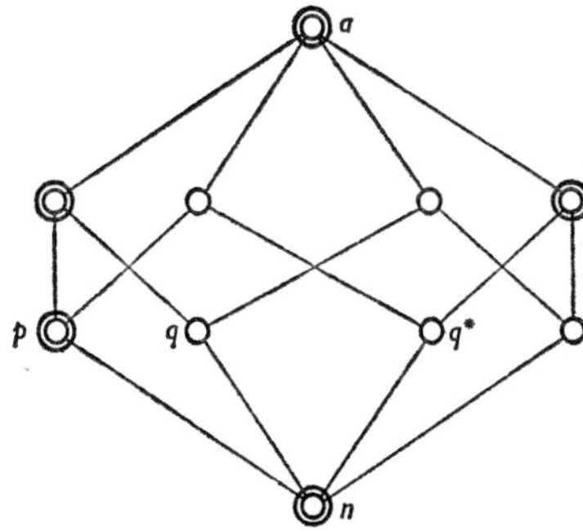

Fig. 59

That the lattice is non-modular can be seen from the fact that the elements emphasized in the figure form a sublattice of type $\bar{m}$.

1.4. Decomposition into atoms

If V is of finite length below, then V is atomic, i.e., for every element a of V there exists an atom (upper neighbour of n) with $p \leqslant a$. The atoms are, of course, irreducible. *If in addition V is segmentwise complemented* (Chapter V, § 6.1), *then only the atoms are irreducible.*

Proof. If a is not an atom, then there is an atom $p \leqslant a$ and in the interval a/n a relative complement q to p:

(1) $$p \sqcup q = a,$$

(2) $$p \sqcap q = n.$$

From (2) it follows that $q \neq a$, because $p \sqcap a = p \neq n$. Hence (1) is a decomposition of a.

In a segmentwise complemented lattice of finite length below every element can be represented as the union of finitely many atoms.

If in addition V is modular and if $\delta(a)=r$ is the dimension of the element a (Chapter V, § 2), *then there is an irredundant representation of a in terms of precisely r atoms.*

Proof. We construct a chain $n < a_1 < \ldots < a$ by setting:

$$a_1 = p_1, \text{ an arbitrary atom } p_1 \leqslant a,$$
$$a_\varrho = a_{\varrho-1}\, p_\varrho,\ p_\varrho \text{ an atom } \leqslant a \text{ with } a_{\varrho-1} \sqcap p_\varrho = n;$$

such a p_ϱ exists as long as $a_{\varrho-1} < a$. Now

$$\delta(a_\varrho) = \delta(a_{\varrho-1}) + \delta(p_\varrho) - \delta(a_{\varrho-1} \sqcap p_\varrho) = \delta(a_{\varrho-1}) + 1 = \varrho.$$

So the method ends after r steps with

$$a_r = p_1 \sqcup \ldots \sqcup p_r = a.$$

In a similar way we can show: *if V is of finite length and modular and if every element has a representation as a union of finitely many atoms, then V is segmentwise complemented.*

Proof. Let $a = p_1 \sqcup \ldots \sqcup p_r$ be an irredundant representation of a in terms of atoms. We shall show that for every $b \leqslant a$ there exists (at least) one element b' with $b \sqcup b' = a$, $b \sqcap b' = n$.

If $b = a$, then $b' = n$ is such an element.

If $b < a$, then among $p_1, \ldots, p_r$ there exists a p_ϱ for which $p_\varrho \nleqslant b$, hence $b \sqcap p_\varrho = n$. We number the p_ϱ so that p_1 is such an atom and we set

$$b_1 = b \sqcup p_1.$$

By the dimension equation

$$\delta(b_1) = \delta(b) + \delta(p_1) - \delta(b \sqcap p_1) = \delta(b) + 1.$$

If $b_1 < a$, then there exists a p_ϱ, and with a suitable numbering p_2, so that $p_2 \nleqslant b_1$, hence $b_1 \sqcap p_2 = n$. $b_2 \leftrightharpoons b_1 \sqcup p_2$ has the dimension $\delta(b)+2$.

The method ends after $s \leqslant r$ steps with $b_s = b \sqcup p_1 \sqcup \ldots \sqcup p_s = a$, and here $\delta(b_s) = \delta(b)+s = r$. For $b' = p_1 \sqcup \ldots \sqcup p_s$ we have therefore: $b \sqcup b' = a$.

Furthermore, the method of construction shows that $\delta(b') = s$, and since now $\delta(b \sqcup b') = \delta(b_s) = \delta(b)+s = \delta(b)+\delta(b')$, it follows from the dimension equation that

$$\delta(b \sqcap b') = 0, \text{ whence } b \sqcap b' = n.$$

§ 2. Embedding theorems

2.1. *Statement of the problem*

Can a lattice be extended so that the larger lattice has certain desirable properties, just as one extends the set of rational numbers to the set of real numbers, so that every sequence satisfying the Cauchy criteria has a limit?

Definition. A formation $(M; R_1, \ldots, R_k)$—see Chapter IV, § 1—is said to be *embedded* in a formation $(M'; R_1, \ldots, R_k)$, i.e. one with the same relations, if $(M; R_1, \ldots, R_k)$ is isomorphic to a subformation of $(M', R_1, \ldots, R_k)$.

Consequences. If a lattice $(V, \sqcap, \sqcup)$ is embedded in $(W, \sqcap, \sqcup)$ and if W is modular or distributive, then V is also modular or distributive, respectively. A non-modular (non-distributive) lattice cannot be embedded in a modular (distributive) lattice. However, completeness or complementarity (at least in distributive lattices) can be attained by embedding in a larger lattice.

2.2. *Embedding of an ordered set in a complete lattice*

Theorem 1. Every ordered set $(M, \leqslant)$ can be embedded in a complete lattice.

Following MacNeille[1] we shall produce this embedding by means of Dedekind cuts.

Preliminary definition. A pair A, B of subsets of M is called a *cut* if

(1) $$\bigwedge_{a \in A} \bigwedge_{b \in B} a \leqslant b,$$

[1] *Trans. Amer. Math. Soc.* **42**, 1937.

(2a) $$\bigwedge_{a \in A} a \leqslant x \rightarrow x \in B,$$

(2b) $$\bigwedge_{b \in B} x \leqslant b \rightarrow x \in A$$

in other words, if B is the set of all upper bounds of A and A the set of all lower bounds of B, in the notation of Chapter II, § 2.1

(3) $$B = \mathsf{Ma}\, A \wedge A = \mathsf{Mi}\, B.$$

For the time being we call A the *lower class*, B the *upper class* of the cut. Obviously a cut is determined by its lower class alone; we therefore call the lower class A itself a cut. The set $\mathfrak{S}$ of cuts of M is then a subset of $\mathfrak{P}M$.

From (3) it follows that

(4) $$A = \mathsf{Mi}(\mathsf{Ma}\, A),$$

whereas for an arbitrary subset N of M we can only state, in general, that

(5) $$N \subseteq \mathsf{Mi}(\mathsf{Ma}\, N).$$

If a subset A of M has the property (4) and if one defines $B = \mathsf{Ma}\, A$, then (1) and (2) are satisfied. Therefore (4) *characterizes* a cut and will be used from now on as the *Definition*.

The relation derived in Chapter II, § 2.1

$$\mathsf{Mi}(\mathsf{Ma}(\mathsf{Mi}\, A)) = \mathsf{Mi}\, A$$

shows that cuts exist. In the subsequent proofs we also need (see loc. cit.)

(6) from $P \subseteq Q (\subseteq M)$ follows $\mathsf{Ma}\, Q \subseteq \mathsf{Ma}\, P$ and $\mathsf{Mi}\, Q \subseteq \mathsf{Mi}\, P$.

Since $\mathfrak{S}$ is a subset of $\mathfrak{P}M$, $\subseteq$ is an order relation in $\mathfrak{S}$. We claim that $(\mathfrak{S}, \subseteq)$ is a complete lattice.

The main part of the proof is

Lemma 1. If for all indices k of an index set K the sets A_k are cuts, then so is their intersection D; in symbols:

$$\bigwedge_{k \in K} A_k \in \mathfrak{S} \rightarrow D = \bigcap_{k \in K} A_k \in \mathfrak{S}.$$

By virtue of (4) we have to show:

(7) $$\mathsf{Mi}(\mathsf{Ma}\, D) \subseteq D.$$

To this end we have

Lemma 2.

$$\mathsf{Ma}\, D = \mathsf{Ma}(\bigcap_{k\in K} A_k) \supseteq \bigcup_{k\in K} \mathsf{Ma}\, A_k.$$

Figure 60 can serve as an illustration.

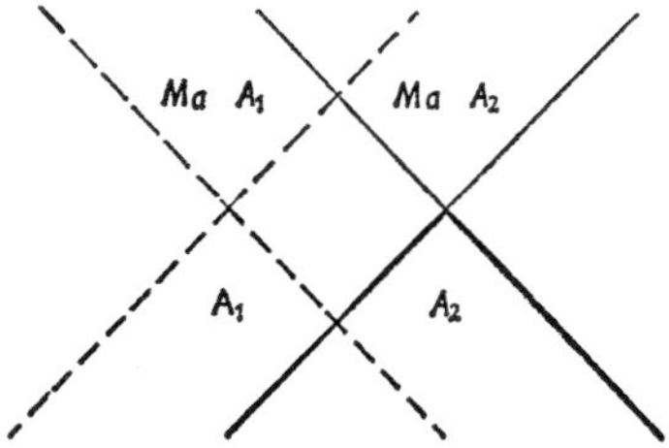

Fig. 60

Proof. By the definition of D

$$\bigwedge_{k\in K} D \subseteq A_k,$$

hence

$$\bigwedge_{k\in K} \mathsf{Ma}\, A_k \subseteq \mathsf{Ma}\, D,$$

i.e.

$$\bigcup_{k\in K} \mathsf{Ma}\, A_k \subseteq \mathsf{Ma}\, D.$$

Proof of Lemma 1. If $x \in \mathsf{Mi}(\mathsf{Ma}\, D)$, then $x \leqslant b$ for all $b \in \mathsf{Ma}\, D$, hence by Lemma 2:

(8) $$x \leqslant b \text{ for all } b \in \bigcup \mathsf{Ma}\, A_k.$$

If $x \notin A_k$, then there is an $i \in K$ such that $x \notin A_l$. Since A_l by assumption is a cut, so that (6) holds, x is not a lower bound of $\mathsf{Ma}\, A_l$, i.e., there is a $b_i \in \mathsf{Ma}\, A_l$ with $x \nleqslant b_l$, in contradiction to (8).

Lemma 1 states that $\mathfrak{S}$ is a complete $\cap$-semilattice. Since M is itself a cut, every set of lower classes has an upper bound, namely M. Therefore by the theorem proved in Chapter II, § 2.2 $\mathfrak{S}$ is a complete lattice.

To show that M is order isomorphic to a subset of $\mathfrak{S}$ we assign to every element a of M the set

$$[a] = \{x; x \leqslant a\}.$$

It is easy to check that $[a]$ is a cut and that the mapping $a \rightarrowtail [a]$ is an order isomorphism. The proof of Theorem 1 is now complete.

For later use we introduce the following concept: a subset Q of an ordered set is called a segment if $q \in Q \wedge x \leqslant q \rightarrow x \in Q$.

$[a]=\{x;\ x\leqslant a\}$ is a segment; we call $[a]$ the *principal segment* generated by a.

2.3. *Embedding of a lattice in a complete lattice*

If $(M, \leqslant)$ is a lattice $(M, \sqcup, \sqcap)$, then it is not certain *a priori* that the method we have indicated yields a lattice embedding. What we have proved is that the complete lattice $(\mathfrak{S}, \subseteq)$ contains a subset $\mathfrak{H}$, the set of principal segments, that is order isomorphic to M. According to Chapter IV, § 1.2 an order isomorphism is at the same time a $\sqcap$- and $\sqcup$-isomorphism. But we still have to investigate whether $(\mathfrak{H}, \subseteq)$ is a sublattice or only a subformation of $(\mathfrak{S}, \subseteq)$. This question will be answered by the following two statements:

1) In $\mathfrak{S}$, by definition, $[a] \sqcap_{\mathfrak{S}} [b]$ is the largest cut contained in $[a]$ and $[b]$. In $\mathfrak{H}$, $[a] \sqcap_{\mathfrak{H}} [b]$ is the largest principal segment contained in $[a]$ and $[b]$. We claim:

$$[a] \sqcap_{\mathfrak{S}} [b] = [a] \cap [b] = [a \sqcap b] = [a] \sqcap_{\mathfrak{H}} [b].$$

(The only difficulty is in clarifying the assertion; the proof is then quite easy.)

a) $[a] \sqcap_{\mathfrak{S}} [b]=[a] \cap [b]$ follows from § 2.2, Lemma 1.

b) $[a] \cap [b]=[a \sqcap b]$; for x is element of $[a] \cap [b]$ if and only if $x\leqslant a \wedge x\leqslant b$. Precisely then we have $x\leqslant a \sqcap b$.

c) Since $[a] \sqcap_{\mathfrak{S}} [b] \in \mathfrak{H}$, the last assertion also follows.

2) We claim: $[a] \sqcup_{\mathfrak{S}} [b]=[a \sqcup b]$.

Proof. a) $[a \sqcup b]$ is a cut containing $[a]$ and $[b]$.

b) We claim: if U is a cut containing $[a]$ and $[b]$, then $[a \sqcup b]\subseteq U$. On account of (6) and (4) it is sufficient to prove

$$\mathsf{Ma}\, U \subseteq \mathsf{Ma}[a \sqcup b].$$

Let $x \in \mathsf{Ma}\, U$; then $x\geqslant u$ for all u in U, hence also $x\geqslant a$ and $x\geqslant b$, i.e., $x\geqslant a \sqcup b$, i.e., $x \in \mathsf{Ma}[a \sqcup b]$.

Note. We also have $[a] \sqcup_{\mathfrak{H}} [b]=[a] \sqcup_{\mathfrak{S}} [b]=[a \sqcup b]$.

2.4. *Ideals and filters*

We compare the notion of a cut with that of an ideal, which comes from the theory of rings.

Definition. A subset $\mathfrak{a}$ of a lattice $(V, \sqcap, \sqcup)$ is called an *ideal* if

(J1) $$x \in \mathfrak{a} \wedge y \in \mathfrak{a} \rightarrow x \sqcup y \in \mathfrak{a},$$

(J2) $$x \in \mathfrak{a} \wedge v \in V \rightarrow x \sqcap v \in \mathfrak{a}.$$

We denote the set of ideals of V by $\mathfrak{J}(V)$. (The analogy to the ring-theoretical concept becomes apparent when one writes $+$ instead of $\sqcup$ and $\cdot$ instead of $\sqcap$.)

Equivalent to (J2) is the statement

(J2′) $\mathfrak{a}$ is a segment, i.e., $x \in \mathfrak{a} \wedge y \subseteq x \rightarrow y \in \mathfrak{a}$.

Proof. (J2) follows from (J2′), because for every $v \in V$ we have $x \sqcap v \leqslant x$.

(J2′) follows from (J2), because if $x \in \mathfrak{a} \wedge y \leqslant x$, then $y = x \sqcap y$, hence by (J2) $y \in \mathfrak{a}$.

Every principal segment $[a]$ also has the property (J1). Therefore we call the principal segments of a lattice *principal ideals.*

It is easy to verify that every cut is an ideal. The fact that not every ideal is a cut is shown by the lattice with the order diagram of Fig. 61. R is the set of numbers $1-1/k$, $k=1,2,3,\ldots$

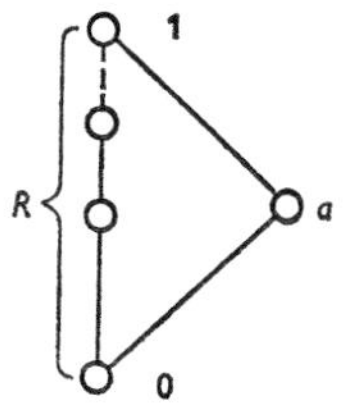

Fig. 61

R is an ideal, but not a cut, because

$$\mathrm{Ma}\,R = \{1\} \text{ and } \mathrm{Mi}(\mathrm{Ma}\,R) = R \cup \{a\}.$$

$(\mathfrak{J}(V), \subseteq)$ is a complete lattice, for we have $\bigsqcup_{k \in K} \mathfrak{a}_k = \bigcap_{k \in K} \mathfrak{a}_k$ and V is itself an ideal. $x \rightarrowtail [x]$ is an isomorphism of V onto a sublattice of $\mathfrak{J}(V)$, hence an embedding of V in a complete lattice.

For a later application we carry through the same arguments for the concept 'filter' dual to the concept 'ideal'. Henceforth we denote filters by small gothic letters, and the set of filters of V by $\mathfrak{F}(V)$.

Definition. A subset $\mathfrak{a}$ of V is called *dual ideal* or *filter* if

(F1) $$x \in \mathfrak{a} \wedge y \in \mathfrak{a} \rightarrow x \sqcap y \in \mathfrak{a},$$

(F2) $$x \in \mathfrak{a} \wedge v \in V \rightarrow x \sqcup v \in \mathfrak{a}.$$

(F2) is equivalent to

(F2′) $$x \in \mathfrak{a} \wedge y \geqslant x \rightarrow y \in \mathfrak{a}.$$

For every x the set $\langle x\rangle = \{z; z \geqslant x\}$ is a filter, the *principal filter* generated by x.

$(\mathfrak{F}(V), \subseteq)$ is a complete lattice, for

$$\bigsqcap_{k\in K} \mathfrak{a}_k = \bigcap_{k\in K} \mathfrak{a}_k$$

and V is a filter.

For principal filters we have: $\langle a\rangle \sqcap \langle b\rangle = \langle a\rangle \cap \langle b\rangle$ consists precisely of those elements x for which $a \leqslant x$ and $b \leqslant x$. Hence

(1) $$\langle a\rangle \sqcap \langle b\rangle = \langle a \sqcup b\rangle.$$

$\mathfrak{a} \sqcup \mathfrak{b}$, the smallest filter containing $\mathfrak{a}$ and $\mathfrak{b}$ contains by (F1) all elements $a \sqcap b$ with $a \in \mathfrak{a}$, $b \in \mathfrak{b}$, and by (F2′) all larger elements, hence

(2) $$\mathfrak{a} \sqcup \mathfrak{b} \subseteq \{x; \bigvee_{a\in\mathfrak{a}} \bigvee_{b\in\mathfrak{b}} a \sqcap b \leqslant x\} \leftrightharpoons \mathfrak{v}.$$

It is easy to see that $\mathfrak{v}$ is a filter (this was anticipated by our notation) and that $\mathfrak{a} \subseteq \mathfrak{v}$ and $\mathfrak{b} \subseteq \mathfrak{v}$; hence

(2′) $$\mathfrak{a} \sqcup \mathfrak{b} = \mathfrak{v}.$$

For principal filters we obtain

(3) $$\langle a\rangle \sqcup \langle b\rangle = \langle a \sqcap b\rangle.$$

On account of (1) and (3) we call the mapping $x \mapsto \langle x\rangle$ a *dual isomorphism* or *anti-isomorphism*, and we say: V can be embedded anti-isomorphically in the complete lattice $\mathfrak{F}(V)$.

Theorem. If V is distributive, then so is $\mathfrak{F}(V)$.

Proof. First of all, in a distributive lattice the representation (2) or (2′), respectively, may be simplified. For $a \sqcap b \leqslant x$ holds if and only if

$$x = (a \sqcap b) \sqcup x = (a \sqcup x) \sqcap (b \sqcup x).$$

But since $a \sqcup x$ is an element of $\mathfrak{a}$ when a is, and $b \sqcup x$ is an element of $\mathfrak{b}$, when b is, therefore

(2″) $$\mathfrak{a} \sqcup \mathfrak{b} = \{a \sqcap b; a \in \mathfrak{a}, b \in \mathfrak{b}\}.$$

Now we claim: $\mathfrak{a} \sqcap (\mathfrak{b} \sqcup \mathfrak{c}) \subseteq (\mathfrak{a} \sqcap \mathfrak{b}) \sqcup (\mathfrak{a} \sqcap \mathfrak{c})$.

Proof. $x \in \mathfrak{a} \sqcap (\mathfrak{b} \sqcup \mathfrak{c})$ means: there exist $a \in \mathfrak{a}$, $b \in \mathfrak{b}$, $c \in \mathfrak{c}$ such that $x = a = b \sqcap c$.

Then $\quad x = a \sqcup (b \sqcap c) = (a \sqcup b) \sqcap (a \sqcup c)$.

Now $\quad a \sqcup b \geqslant a$, $a \sqcup b \geqslant b$, hence $a \sqcup b \in \mathfrak{a} \sqcap \mathfrak{b}$.

And similarly $a \sqcup c \in \mathfrak{a} \sqcap \mathfrak{c}$, hence $x \in (\mathfrak{a} \sqcap \mathfrak{b}) \sqcup (\mathfrak{a} \sqcap \mathfrak{c})$.

2.5. *Embedding of a distributive lattice in a complemented lattice*

We discuss only the case of a distributive lattice, because only then is the complement uniquely determined. In a certain sense Leibniz may be said to have treated this problem. He attempted to develop a logical calculus by assigning numbers to concepts—co-prime numbers to distinct concepts—expressing the composition of concepts by the product of the numbers, for example

$$6 = \textit{animal}, \quad 5 = \textit{rationale}, \quad 30 = \textit{homo}.$$

He then writes $30 \sqcap 6 \cdot 5$ for: *homo est animal rationale.*[1]

We know that in this way we obtain a distributive lattice. In order to introduce a negation we have to embed it in a complemented lattice. Leibniz tried to do this—of course not in our notation—by assigning to the concepts not only numbers but number pairs. We could interpret this as the attempt to embed V in the direct product $V \times V$. Naturally, we cannot expect that Leibniz took more than the first groping steps.

A constructive method of embedding, even more generally, a quasi-ordered set in an ortho-complemented lattice has been given by P. Lorenzen.[2] True, it is not sufficient to form pairs of elements, but one has to form again the set of pairs of this set of pairs, etc. The method then allows us to reach conclusions by induction. We cannot dwell here on the details. Let us only mention that W. Peremans[3] has given a similar method for the embedding of a distributive lattice in a Boolean algebra. These constructions yield (in a certain sense) the smallest (ortho-) complemented (semi-)lattice into which the given lattice can be embedded.

[1] 'Opuscules et fragments inédits', éd. Couturat, Paris 1903, p.325.

[2] P. Lorenzen, 'Algebraische und logistische Untersuchungen über freie Verbände', *J. Symbol. Logic* **16**, 1951, 81–106.

[3] W. Peremans, 'Embedding of a distributive lattice into a Boolean algebra', *Indagationes Math.* **19**, 1957, 73–81.

We shall attack the question in a different way, by asking under what condition a lattice V is a *set lattice*, i.e., when there is for a given V a set M such that $(V, \sqcap, \sqcup)$ is isomorphic to a sublattice $(\mathfrak{U}, \cap, \cup)$ of $(\mathfrak{P}M, \cap, \cup)$—with the *set-theoretical* operations $\cap$, $\cup$. Since $\mathfrak{P}M$ is complemented, V is then embedded in a complemented lattice.

Since $\mathfrak{P}M$ is distributive, V must in any case be distributive. It can be shown that this condition is also sufficient.

Now the set of cuts $\mathfrak{S}(V)$ is a subset of $\mathfrak{P}V$, but only a subformation of $(\mathfrak{P}V, \subseteq)$, not a sublattice of $(\mathfrak{P}V, \cap, \cup)$, for in general $A \sqcup_{\mathfrak{S}} B \neq$ $\neq A \cup B$. The theorems of § 1 offer another starting point. If every element x of V can be represented as a $\sqcup$ of irreducible elements, then with x one can associate the set of those irreducible elements from which it is built up, or what proves to be simpler, the set of irreducible elements p with $p \leqslant x$.

We begin with the assumptions:

I. V is distributive.

II. V contains irreducible elements; the set of irreducible elements is called P.

III. Every element of V can be represented as a $\sqcup$ of finitely many elements in P.

With every $x \in V$ we associate the set

$$\varphi x \leftrightharpoons \{p; p \in P, p \leqslant x\}.$$

We set φV, i.e., the set of images of all elements of V, is a subset of $\mathfrak{P}P$.

We claim:

1) $$\varphi(x \sqcap y) = \varphi x \cap \varphi y.$$

Proof. $p \leqslant x \sqcap y$ holds if and only if $p \leqslant x$ and $p \leqslant y$, i.e.,

$$p \in \varphi(x \sqcap y) \leftrightarrow p \in \varphi(x) \wedge p \in \varphi(y).$$

2) $$\varphi(x \sqcup y) = \varphi x \cup \varphi y.$$

Proof. Since V is distributive and p irreducible, Lemma 1 of § 1.2 holds:

$$p \leqslant x \sqcup y \rightarrow p \leqslant x \vee p \leqslant y.$$

From the definition of $\sqcup$ it follows that

$$p \leqslant x \vee p \leqslant y \rightarrow p \leqslant x \sqcup y.$$

3) The mapping φ is uniquely invertible, namely the inverse is:

$$\varphi x \rightarrowtail \bigsqcup_{p \in \varphi x} p.$$

To prove this we have to show that $\bigsqcup_{\varphi x} p$ exists and is equal to x.

a) $$\bigwedge_{p \in \varphi x} p \leqslant x.$$

b) x can be represented as $\sqcup$ of finitely many p in φx, i.e., there exists a finite set $\mu x \subseteq \varphi x$ with $x = \bigsqcup_{p \in \mu x} p$.

But if $\bigwedge_{p \in \varphi x} p \leqslant y$, then also $\bigwedge_{p \in \mu x} p \leqslant y$, i.e., $x \leqslant y$.

a) and b) show that x satisfies the definition of $\bigsqcup_{p \in \varphi x} p$.

In this way $(V, \sqcap, \sqcup)$ is mapped isomorphically onto $(\varphi V, \cap, \cup)$, and this is a sublattice of $(\mathfrak{P}P, \cap, \cup)$.

We can free ourselves of the assumptions II and III by first embedding V anti-isomorphically in the lattice of filters $\mathfrak{F}(V)$ and then $\mathfrak{F}(V)$ again anti-isomorphically in a set lattice. (Why we did not choose the 'direct' way via $\mathfrak{J}(V)$ is explained in the footnote on page 166.) On the basis of the specific properties of filters it can be shown that $\mathfrak{F}(V)$ contains completely $\sqcap$-irreducible elements; however, this requires an application of the maximal principle (Zorn's Lemma). Then an argument corresponding to the one we have just given can be carried through.

So we first prove the existence of completely $\sqcap$-irreducible elements in $\mathfrak{F}(V)$.

Let $\mathfrak{M}(\mathfrak{x}, d)$ be the set of all filters containing a given filter $\mathfrak{x}$ and not containing a given element $d (\notin x)$ of V. Since $\mathfrak{x} \in \mathfrak{M}(\mathfrak{x}, d)$, $\mathfrak{M}(\mathfrak{x}, d)$ is not empty.

Assertion 1. If $\mathfrak{L}$ is a linearly ordered (by $\subseteq$) subset of $\mathfrak{M}$, then $\mathfrak{v} = \bigcup_{\mathfrak{l} \in \mathrm{L}} \mathfrak{l}$ is an element of $\mathfrak{M}$.

Proof. a) Obviously $\mathfrak{x} \subseteq \mathfrak{v}$ and $d \notin \mathfrak{v}$.

b) $\mathfrak{v}$ is a filter; for

b1) $x \in \mathfrak{v}$ and $y \in \mathfrak{v}$ means: there exist $\mathfrak{l}_1$, $\mathfrak{l}_2$ in $\mathfrak{L}$ such that $x \in \mathfrak{l}_1$, $y \in \mathfrak{l}_2$.

Since $\mathfrak{L}$ is linearly ordered, we have $\mathfrak{l}_1 \subseteq \mathfrak{l}_2$, say, hence also $x \in \mathfrak{l}_2$. This implies $x \sqcap y \in \mathfrak{l}_2 \subseteq \mathfrak{v}$.

b2) If $x \in \mathfrak{v}$, i.e. $x \in \mathfrak{l}_1$, say, and $v \in V$, then $x \sqcup v \in \mathfrak{l}_1 \subseteq \mathfrak{v}$.

Now by the maximal principle we have

Assertion 2. $\mathfrak{M}(\mathfrak{x}, d)$ has a maximal element, i.e., there exists a filter $\mathfrak{p}$ with $\mathfrak{x} \subseteq \mathfrak{p}$, $d \notin \mathfrak{p}$ such that $\mathfrak{p} \subseteq \mathfrak{v} \wedge d \in \mathfrak{b} \rightarrow \mathfrak{p} = \mathfrak{b}$.

Assertion 3. $\mathfrak{p}$ is completely $\sqcap$-irreducible, i.e.,

$$\mathfrak{p} = \bigsqcap_{\mathfrak{b}\in\mathfrak{B}} \mathfrak{b} = \bigcap_{\mathfrak{b}\in\mathfrak{B}} \mathfrak{b} \to \bigvee_{\mathfrak{b}\in\mathfrak{B}} \mathfrak{b} = \mathfrak{p}, \quad (\mathfrak{B} \subseteq \mathfrak{F}(V)).$$

Proof. From the assumption it follows that $\bigwedge_{\mathfrak{b}\in\mathfrak{B}} (\mathfrak{x} \subseteq \mathfrak{p} \subseteq \mathfrak{b})$. If $\bigwedge_{\mathfrak{b}\in\mathfrak{B}} d \in \mathfrak{b}$, then $d \in \mathfrak{p}$. Hence there exists a $\mathfrak{b}_0 \in \mathfrak{B}$ with $\mathfrak{p} \subseteq \mathfrak{b}_0$ and $d \notin \mathfrak{b}_0$.

From Assertion 2 it then follows that $\mathfrak{p} = \mathfrak{b}_0$.

So we have shown that $\mathfrak{F}(V)$ contains completely $\sqcap$-irreducible elements, in fact for every $\mathfrak{x}$ and $d \notin x$ a $\mathfrak{p}$ with $\mathfrak{x} \subseteq \mathfrak{p}$, $d \notin \mathfrak{p}$.[1]

We denote the set of completely $\sqcap$-irreducible filters by P and associate with every filter $\mathfrak{x}$ the set

$$\varphi\mathfrak{x} = \{\mathfrak{p}; \mathfrak{p} \in P, \mathfrak{x} \subseteq \mathfrak{p}\}.$$

Assertion 4. The mapping $\mathfrak{x} \mapsto \varphi\mathfrak{x}$ is an anti-isomorphism of $\mathfrak{F}(V)$ onto a sublattice of $(\mathfrak{P}P, \cup, \cap)$.

Proof. a) $\mathfrak{p} \in \varphi(\mathfrak{x} \sqcup \mathfrak{y}) \leftrightarrow \mathfrak{x} \sqcup \mathfrak{p} \subseteq \mathfrak{p} \leftrightarrow \mathfrak{x} \subseteq \mathfrak{p} \wedge \mathfrak{y} \subseteq \mathfrak{p}$,

i.e. $\mathfrak{p} \in (\varphi\mathfrak{x} \cap \varphi\mathfrak{y})$.

b) $\mathfrak{p} \in \varphi(\mathfrak{x} \sqcap \mathfrak{y})$ means that $\mathfrak{x} \sqcap \mathfrak{y} \subseteq \mathfrak{p}$,

i.e. $\mathfrak{p} = \mathfrak{p} \sqcup (\mathfrak{x} \sqcap \mathfrak{y}) = (\mathfrak{p} \sqcup \mathfrak{x}) \sqcap (\mathfrak{p} \sqcup \mathfrak{y})$.

(Here we use the distribution law.)

Since $\mathfrak{p}$ is $\sqcap$-irreducible, this holds if and only if $\mathfrak{p} = \mathfrak{p} \sqcup \mathfrak{x}$ or $\mathfrak{p} = \mathfrak{p} \sqcup \mathfrak{y}$, i.e., if $\mathfrak{x} \subseteq \mathfrak{p}$ or $\mathfrak{y} \subseteq \mathfrak{p}$. Hence $\varphi(\mathfrak{x} \sqcap \mathfrak{y}) = \varphi\mathfrak{x} \cup \varphi\mathfrak{y}$.

c) φ is uniquely invertible; the inverse mapping is $\varphi\mathfrak{x} \mapsto \bigsqcap_{\varphi\mathfrak{x}} \mathfrak{p}$.

Since $\mathfrak{F}(V)$ is a complete lattice, we do not have to prove separately the existence of $\bigsqcap \mathfrak{p}$. But we do have to prove that $\bigsqcap_{\varphi\mathfrak{x}} \mathfrak{p} = \mathfrak{x}$.

Proof. Since $\bigwedge_{\mathfrak{p}\in\varphi\mathfrak{x}} \mathfrak{x} \subseteq \mathfrak{p}$, we have $\mathfrak{x} \subseteq \bigsqcap_{\varphi\mathfrak{x}} \mathfrak{p} = \bigcap_{\varphi\mathfrak{x}} \mathfrak{p} \leftrightharpoons \mathfrak{d}$.

If $\mathfrak{x} \subset \mathfrak{d}$, then there exists a $d \in \mathfrak{d}$, $d \notin \mathfrak{x}$.

[1] The $\sqcup$-irreducible ideals would have to be characterized by the fact that (they are contained in a given ideal and) the set of their upper bounds does not contain the given element d. In addition one would have to operate with $\sqcup$, the definition of which is somewhat more complicated than that of $\sqcap = \cap$.

By Assertions 2 and 3 there is then a $\mathfrak{p}$ with $\mathfrak{x}\subseteq\mathfrak{p}$ (i.e., $\mathfrak{p}\in\varphi\mathfrak{x}$) and $d\notin\mathfrak{p}$.

This implies $$d\notin\mathfrak{d}.$$

Since V is mapped anti-isomorphically onto a sublattice of $\mathfrak{F}(V)$, $\mathfrak{F}(V)$ anti-isomorphically onto a sublattice of $(\mathfrak{P}P,\cap,\cup)$, V is mapped isomorphically onto a sublattice of $(\mathfrak{P}P,\cap,\cup)$.

§ 3. Embedding of a lattice in a direct product. Application to the theory of divisibility

3.1. Embedding in a direct product

The direct product of the lattices $(V_s,\sqcap_s,\sqcup_s)$, $s\in S$, in symbols $\prod_S V_s$, consists of the 'vectors' $\mathfrak{x}=(\ldots,x_s,\ldots)$ that contain precisely one element x_s from every V_s as s-component, with the operations

$$(1)\qquad \mathfrak{x}\sqcap\mathfrak{y}=(\ldots,x_s\sqcap_s y_s,\ldots),\quad \mathfrak{x}\sqcup\mathfrak{y}=(\ldots,x_s\sqcup_s y_s,\ldots).$$

We ask under what conditions a given lattice can be represented as a direct product.

If $\mathfrak{V}\subseteq\prod V_s$, then there are congruence relations K_s in $\mathfrak{V}$ defined by $\mathfrak{x}K_s\mathfrak{y}\leftrightarrows x_s=y_s$.

We have $$\mathfrak{x}=\mathfrak{y}\leftrightarrow\bigwedge_s\mathfrak{x}K_s\mathfrak{y},\text{ i.e., }\mathfrak{x}\bigsqcap_S K_s\mathfrak{y}.$$

If we denote equality (as in Chapter V, § 5.1, page 89) by D, we can write this as

$$(2)\qquad D=\bigsqcap_S K_s.$$

Conversely, if for a lattice V there exists a set of congruences K_s satisfying (2), then we can assign to every element x of V the equivalence classes $x_s=\{z;zK_sx\}$. If in the set of vectors $(\ldots,x_s,\ldots)$ we define the order relation as above under (1), then the mapping

$$x\rightarrow\mathfrak{x}=(\ldots,x_s,\ldots)$$

is a homomorphism with respect to $\sqcap$ and $\sqcup$, and on account of (2) an isomorphism of V onto a sublattice of $\prod V_s$. Hence a lattice can be embedded in a direct product if there exists a representation of D as $\sqcap$ (conjunction) of congruences.

For V to be isomorphic to $\prod V_s$, additional postulates are necessary. In case S is finite, the following is sufficient:

(3) $K_s K_t = U$ for arbitrary s and t in S, $s \neq t$. (U is the all relation valid for all pairs x, y (see Chapter V, § 5.1).)

From (3) it follows that:

(3a) The congruences K_s are *permutable.*

(3b) For any two distinct s and t in S: $K_s \sqcup K_t = U$; therefore the K_s are called *co-prime.*

We have to prove: 1) (3) is satisfied in $\prod V_s$. For every pair $\mathfrak{x}$, $\mathfrak{y}$ of $\prod V_s$ there exists a $\mathfrak{z}$ with $\mathfrak{x} K_s \mathfrak{z} \wedge \mathfrak{z} K_t \mathfrak{y}$; we only have to set $z_s = x_s$, $z_t = y_t$.

2) If (3) is satisfied, then V is isomorphic to $\prod V_s$, provided S is a finite set. The proof is now by induction: x_s is the class of elements congruent to x modulo K_s; we have $x \in x_s$; let x_s be represented by the element a_s. Then we claim: for every system $(x_s, s \in S)$, i.e., every system $(a_s, s \in S)$ there exists an element x in V with $x K_s a_s$ for all s.

If S consists of only two elements, this follows immediately from (3): $K_1 K_2 = U$ means: for every pair a_1, a_2 there exists an x with

$$a_1 K_1 x \wedge x K_2 a_2.$$

If S consists of three elements, then it follows from (3b) that

$$(K_1 \sqcup K_2) \sqcap (K_1 \sqcup K_3) = U$$

and from the fact that the congruences of a lattice form a distributive lattice that

$$K_1 \sqcup (K_2 \sqcap K_3) = U.$$

Consequently K_1 and $K_2 \sqcap K_3 = K_2'$ form a system of two congruences with (2) and (3); therefore V can be represented as a direct product of V_1 and V_2'. In V_2' new congruence relations are induced by K_2, K_3, and they allow a further decomposition. This sketch of the inductive method may suffice.

For the case of an infinite set S we refer to the literature (Dilworth, 'Lattice Theory', 1961).

3.2. *Applications to the theory of divisibility. Statement of the problem*

In Chapter III, § 2.2 it was shown that the lattice of natural numbers with divisibility as the order relation is a sublattice of the direct product of linearly ordered sets. (To emphasize that linearly ordered sets are lattices we call them *linear lattices.*) Here the order relation is defined by means of a given operation (multiplication).

A formation $(G, \cdot, \leqslant)$ which is a group (or semigroup, respectively) under multiplication and a lattice under $\leqslant$, where an additional relation between $\cdot$ and $\leqslant$ has to be postulated, is called a *lattice group* (or semigroup, respectively). (More precise statements will follow in the next section.) The question by which we generalize the theory of divisibility is the following: *under what conditions can a lattice group be embedded in the direct product of linear lattice groups?*

Since linear lattices and direct products of them are distributive, it must be postulated that the lattice group is a distributive lattice. It turns out that this is the case in every lattice group. Since the congruences of a group are permutable (see Chapter V, § 5.3), condition (3a) of the preceding section is satisfied. Therefore our task is to find in the set of congruences some that satisfy condition (3b), whose conjunction is D, and whose residue classes are linearly ordered by the order of G.

Instead of starting from the equality relation D and the congruence relation one can also start from the order relation. This has been done by P. Lorenzen in a number of papers.[1] In the direct product of the lattices $(V_s, \leqslant_s)$ the order is given by

$$\mathfrak{x} \leqslant \mathfrak{y} \leftrightharpoons \bigwedge_s x_s \leqslant_s y_s.$$

By

$$\mathfrak{x} R_s \mathfrak{y} \leftrightharpoons x_s \leqslant_s y_s$$

quasi-orders are defined whose conjunction is the order $\leqslant$. R_s and K_s are linked by the relation $K_s = R_s \sqcap \tilde{R}_s$.

On resolving the natural numbers into prime factors,

$$a = p_1^{\alpha_1} p_2^{\alpha_2} \ldots, \quad p_i \text{ prime}, p_i < p_{i+1},$$

we obtain the quasi-orders

$$a R_s b \leftrightharpoons \alpha_s \underset{z}{\leqslant} \beta_s,$$

which correspond to the 'valuations'. The lattice-theoretical interpretation allows a generalization of this concept.

Our question is when can the order $\leqslant$ of $(G, \cdot, \leqslant)$ be represented

[1] We mention in particular:
'Über halbgeordnete Gruppen', *Math. Z.* **52**, 1950, 483–526.
'Teilbarkeitstheorie in Bereichen', *Math. Z.* **55**, 1952, 269–275.
'Die Erweiterung halbgeordneter Gruppen zu Verbandsgruppen', *Math. Z.* **58**, 1953, 15–24.

as a conjunction of linear quasi-orders. A necessary and sufficient condition turns out to be

$$a \sqcap xax^{-1} = 1 \rightarrow a = 1.$$

We can give only a brief account of this theory, but we wish to develop at least its initial stages in more detail.

3.3. Lattice groups

Definition. A set G with an operation '$\cdot$' is called a *semigroup* if the operation is associative and if G contains an element 1 with the property $1 \cdot x = x \cdot 1 = x$ for all $x \in G$. If for every element x an inverse x^{-1} with $xx^{-1} = x^{-1}x = 1$ exists, then $(G, \cdot)$ is a group. $(G, \cdot, \leqslant)$ is called a *quasi-ordered group* if $\leqslant$ is a quasi-order (i.e. reflexive and transitive) and *monotonic* (or compatible with the operation), i.e., if for all a, b, x, y of G

$$(M1) \qquad a \leqslant b \wedge x \leqslant y \rightarrow ax \leqslant by.$$

It is easy to check that $(M1)$ is equivalent to

$$(M2) \qquad a \leqslant b \rightarrow xay \leqslant xby.$$

If $\leqslant$ is in addition anti-symmetric, then $(G, \cdot, \leqslant)$ is called an *ordered group*.

Theorem 1a. In a quasi-ordered group the set $H = \{x; 1 \leqslant x\}$ is a semigroup with the property

$$(1) \qquad h \in H \rightarrow \bigwedge_{x \in G} x^{-1}hx \in H.$$

A semigroup with the property (1) is called an *invariant sub-semigroup* of G.

Theorem 1b. If H is an invariant sub-semigroup of G, then G with

$$(2) \qquad a \leqslant b \leftrightharpoons a^{-1}b \in H$$

is a quasi-ordered group.

For the proof we need the *lemma*: If 1 is the 1-element of G and H an invariant sub-semigroup, then $1 \in H$.

Proof. By definition H contains an element e_H with $e_H x = x e_H = x$ for all x in H. Now

$$1 = e_H^{-1} e_H = e_H^{-1} e_H e_H \in H$$

by (1). Of course, then also $e_H = 1$.

Now the reflexivity of $\leqslant$ follows: $a^{-1}a=1 \in H$. The remaining proofs of Theorem 1a and 1b are left to the reader.

The elements of H are called the *integral* elements of G (relative to H). $\leqslant$ is also read as 'divides'.

From the monotonic law it follows that

(3) $$a \leqslant b \rightarrow ab^{-1} \leqslant 1 \leqslant a^{-1}b$$

and in particular for $b=1$

(4) $$a \leqslant 1 \rightarrow 1 \leqslant a^{-1}.$$

The quasi-order defined by H is anti-symmetric, hence an order, if for all a of G

(5) $$a \in H \wedge a^{-1} \in H \rightarrow a = 1.$$

The quasi-order defined by H is linear if for all a of G

(6) $$a \in H \vee a^{-1} \in H.$$

For it follows from (6) that for two arbitrary elements a and b of G either $a^{-1}b \in H$ or $(a^{-1}b)^{-1}=b^{-1}a \in H$.

Theorem 2. If $(G, \cdot, \leqslant)$ is an ordered group and a $\sqcap$-semilattice (i.e., if $a \sqcap b$ exists for any two elements), then $(G, \cdot, \leqslant)$ is a lattice, and $a \sqcup b=(a^{-1} \sqcap b^{-1})^{-1}$.

Proof. We have $a^{-1} \sqcap b^{-1} \leqslant a^{-1}$, hence $a \leqslant (a^{-1} \sqcap b^{-1})^{-1}$.

Similarly $$b \leqslant (a^{-1} \sqcap b^{-1})^{-1}.$$

On the other hand, if $a \leqslant x$ and $b \leqslant x$, then $x^{-1} \leqslant a^{-1}$ and $x^{-1} \leqslant b^{-1}$, hence $x^{-1} \leqslant a^{-1} \sqcap b^{-1}$, i.e., $(a^{-1} \sqcap b^{-1})^{-1} \leqslant x$.

$(G, \cdot, \leqslant)$ is then called a *lattice group*.

Theorem 3. In a lattice group the distributive laws hold

(D1) $$x(a \sqcap b) = xa \sqcap xb; \quad (a \sqcap b)x = ax \sqcap bx,$$

(D2) $$x(a \sqcap b) = xa \sqcap xb; \quad (a \sqcap b)x = ax \sqcap bx,$$

and in particular

(D3) $$a \sqcup (b \sqcap c) = (a \sqcup b) \sqcap (a \sqcup c).$$

Proof of (D1). We have $a \sqcap b \leqslant a$, hence $x(a \sqcap b) \leqslant xa$,

$a \sqcap b \leqslant b$, hence $x(a \sqcap b) \leqslant xb$,

therefore (i) $x(a \sqcap b) \leqslant xa \sqcap xb$.

This holds for arbitrary x, a, b; hence also

$$x^{-1}(xa \sqcap xb) \leqslant x^{-1}xa \sqcap x^{-1}xb = a \sqcap b,$$

therefore (*ii*) $xa \sqcap xb \leqslant x(a \sqcap b)$.

From (*i*) and (*ii*) the first assertion of (D1) follows. The remaining assertions of (D1) and (D2) are proved similarly.

For the proof of (D3) we use

Theorem 4. For every c in G there exist two elements a and b in G with $c=ab^{-1}$, $a\geqslant 1$, $b\geqslant 1$, $a \sqcap b=1$.

a and b are uniquely determined by these conditions.

Note. In the notation of the theory of divisibility one reads

$\leqslant$ as 'divides',

$\sqcap$ as 'greatest common divisor',

$a \sqcap b = 1$ as 'a is co-prime to b',

$a \geqslant 1$ as 'a is integral'.

Theorem 4 then reads: Every element of G can be represented in one and only one way as the quotient of two co-prime integral elements.

Proof. Let $c = ab^{-1}$ and $a \sqcap b = 1$;

then $$a = cb,$$

$$1 = a \sqcap b = cb \sqcap b = (c \sqcap 1)b,$$

hence $b^{-1}=c \sqcap 1$, $b=(c \sqcap 1)^{-1}=1 \sqcup c^{-1}$ (compare the characterization of $\sqcup$ in Theorem 2).

Then we have $a = cb = c \sqcup 1$.

Therefore, if elements a and b with the required properties exist, then we can only have $a=1 \sqcup c$, $b=1 \sqcup c^{-1}$. But it is easy to verify that these elements have, in fact, the required properties. $1 \sqcup c$ can be called the *numerator*, $1 \sqcup c^{-1}$ the *denominator* of c.

For later use we note: for every $c \in G$

(7) $$c = (1 \sqcup c)(1 \sqcap c),$$

(8) $$(1 \sqcup c) \sqcap (1 \sqcup c^{-1}) = 1.$$

Theorem 5. The numerator of the greatest common divisor of two elements is equal to the greatest common divisor of their numerators, i.e.

(9) $$1 \sqcup (x \sqcap y) = (1 \sqcup x) \sqcap (1 \sqcup y).$$

We denote the left-hand side of this equation by L, the right-hand side by R. In every lattice $L \leqslant R$; so we only have to prove $R \leqslant L$.

For this purpose we multiply by

$$\begin{aligned} q &= 1 \sqcap (x \sqcap y) = (1 \sqcap x) \sqcap (1 \sqcap y). \\ L \cdot q &= [1 \sqcup (x \sqcap y)][1 \sqcap (x \sqcap y)] = x \sqcap y \qquad \text{by (7)}, \\ R \cdot q &= [(1 \sqcup x) \sqcap (1 \sqcup y)][(1 \sqcap x) \sqcap (1 \sqcap y)] \\ &= (1 \sqcup x)(1 \sqcap x) \sqcap (1 \sqcup y)(1 \sqcap y) \sqcap \ldots \leqslant x \sqcap y = L \cdot q. \end{aligned}$$

Multiplication by q^{-1} yields $R \leqslant L$.

Now we obtain (D3) by setting in (9) $x = a^{-1}b$, $y = a^{-1}c$ and multiplying by a.

3.4. *Embedding of an ordered group in a lattice*

In the case of algebraic number fields a lattice group does not always exist *a priori*. For example, if Q is the field of rational numbers, $Q(\sqrt{-5})$ the extension field obtained by the adjunction of $\sqrt{-5}$, then by means of the integral domain $H = \{a + b\sqrt{-5};\ a$ and b integers$\}$ a quasi-order can be introduced by $x \leqslant y \Leftrightarrow x^{-1}y \in H$. It becomes an order of the multiplicative group of $Q(\sqrt{-5})$ when elements differing only by factors dividing 1 are identified.

In this ordered group there is, for instance, no least common multiple of 3 and $2 + \sqrt{-5}$. So the question arises: can an ordered group $(G, \cdot, \leqslant)$ be embedded in a lattice group?

There are algebraic criteria for this that require concepts which cannot be assumed here. However, the task of constructing a lattice group in which G can be embedded, provided it exists at all, is of a more lattice-theoretical nature.

First of all G is extended to a semilattice-semigroup H in which for an arbitrary finite set of elements a $\sqcap$ always exists. For this we only use the fact that G is a semigroup, i.e., we make no use of the existence of the inverse.

We choose the finite sequences of elements of G as elements of a set $H^* = \{(a_1, \ldots, a_m);\ a_\mu \in G\}$. In H^* we define an order relation $\underset{H}{\leqslant}$. This can be done in various ways, two of which we indicate here:

Definition. $(a_1, \ldots, a_k) \underset{H}{\leqslant} (b_1, \ldots, b_l)$ holds if either

(1) for every b_λ an a_κ exists with $a_\kappa \leqslant b_\lambda$; or

(2) for all x, y, z of G we have

$$\bigwedge_{\kappa} z \leqslant xa_\kappa y \to \bigwedge_{\lambda} z \leqslant xb_\lambda y.$$

We only discuss the second possibility.

One sees immediately that $\underset{H}{\leqslant}$ is reflexive and transitive. To secure anti-symmetry we define:
$(a_1,\dots,a_k)\underset{H}{=}(b_1,\dots,b_l)$ if both the relations $\underset{H}{\leqslant}$ and $\underset{H}{\geqslant}$ hold. Let H be the set of classes of this equivalence relation.

For sequences of single elements we have $(a)\underset{H}{\leqslant}(b)$ if and only if $a\leqslant b$.

Proof. a) From $a\leqslant b$ it follows that $\bigwedge_{x,y} xay\leqslant xby$, whence for all z:

$$z \leqslant xay \to z \leqslant xby.$$

b) If $a\underset{H}{\leqslant} b$ holds, then the definition can be applied to $z=a$, $x=y=1$.

From this it follows further: $(a)\underset{H}{=}(b)\leftrightarrow a=b$. Thus $(G,\leqslant)$ is order-isomorphically mapped onto the subset $(G_1,\underset{H}{\leqslant})$ of $(H,\underset{H}{\leqslant})$, where G_1 consists of the single element sequences. Therefore we need no longer distinguish between G and G_1 and can also omit the letter H in $\underset{H}{\leqslant}$ and $\underset{H}{=}$.

From the definition of $\underset{H}{\leqslant}$ it follows that

$$\bigwedge_{\kappa} (a_1,\dots,a_k) \leqslant a_\kappa$$

and

$$\bigwedge_{\kappa} u \leqslant a_\kappa \to u \leqslant (a_1,\dots,a_k).$$

Hence $$(a_1,\dots,a_k) = a_1 \sqcap a_2 \sqcap \dots \sqcap a_k.$$

Consequently the $\sqcap$ of an arbitrary finite set of elements of G exists, and it is clear how the $\sqcap$ of finitely many elements of H has to be formed. This operation is commutative and associative.

A multiplication in H can be defined by

$$(a_1,\dots,a_k)(b_1,\dots,b_l) = (a_1b_1, a_1b_2,\dots,a_kb_l).$$

It is associative, contains the 1-element of G as 1-element, and its monotonic character is easily checked.

Now H is extended once more dually to a domain in which the $\sqcup$ of finitely many elements always exists. Lorenzen has proved: If the given ordered group admits an embedding in a lattice group, then the construction indicated leads to the goal. (In the second step the 'second possibility' must be used, of course dually.)

3.5. *Embedding of a lattice group in the direct product of linearly ordered groups*

After embedding an ordered group in a lattice group we have by § 1.2 the theorem that every element can be represented as a $\sqcup$ (least common multiple) of irreducible elements. (Among the natural numbers the irreducible elements are the prime powers, in the theory of ideals the primary ideals.) But the theorem of the unique decomposition of a number into prime factors asserts more, namely not only that the lattice group is distributive, but that it can be embedded in the direct product of linear lattice groups. We have already stated the task as follows: the order of G must be the conjunction of linear quasi-orders.

To find out what conditions G must then satisfy we have first of all to characterize the linearly ordered groups. Every linearly ordered set is a lattice, every linearly ordered group a lattice group. In the latter we have

(1) $$c \sqcap z^{-1}c^{-1}z \leqslant 1 \text{ for all } c \text{ and } z.$$

Proof. By § 3.3 (6), page 171, either $c \leqslant 1$ or $c^{-1} \leqslant 1$, and in the second case by monotony $z^{-1}c^{-1}z \leqslant 1$.

(1) is equivalent with

(2) $x_1ax_2 \sqcap y_1by_2 \leqslant x_1bx_2 \sqcup y_1ay_2$ for all a, b, x_1, x_2, y_1, y_2.

Proof. a) (2) follows from (1):

$$(x_1ax_2 \sqcap y_1by_2)(x_2^{-1}b^{-1}x_1^{-1} \sqcap y_2^{-1}a^{-1}y_1^{-1}) \leqslant x_1ab^{-1}x_1^{-1} \sqcap y_1ba^{-1}y_1^{-1} \leqslant 1 \qquad \text{by (1)}$$

(set $x_1ab^{-1}x_1^{-1} = c$ and $x_1y_1^{-1} = z$).

b) (1) follows from (2):

In (2) we set $a = c$, $x_1 = z$, $y_2 = c^{-1}z$, $x^2 = y_1 = b = 1$, and obtain

$$zc \sqcap c^{-1}z \leqslant z \sqcup z = z,$$

hence

$$c \sqcap z^{-1}c^{-1}z \leqslant 1.$$

(1) or (2) also hold for the direct product of linearly ordered lattice groups and are therefore a necessary condition for G to be embeddable in such a direct product. We shall show that this condition is also sufficient.

To simplify the notation we set

$$x_1 a x_2 = \xi a,$$

more accurately: with every pair x_1, x_2 we associate the mapping ξ:

$$a \not\rightarrow \xi a = x_1 a x_2.$$

From the monotonic character, § 3.3 (M2), and the distributive laws § 3.3 (D1), (D2) it follows that these mappings are lattice homomorphisms

(3,1) $$a \leqslant b \rightarrow \xi a \leqslant \xi b,$$

(3,2) $$\xi(a \sqcap b) = \xi a \sqcap \xi b, \; \xi(a \sqcup b) = \xi a \sqcup \xi b.$$

For these homomorphisms (operators) we use the letters ξ, η, ζ. In this notation (2) takes the form:

(2′) $$\xi a \sqcap \eta b \leqslant \xi b \sqcup \eta a.$$

A lattice group in which (2) holds is said to be *regular*.

Apart from the given order $\leqslant$ of G, which we shall now also denote by R, we consider other quasi-orders of G. A quasi-order S is said to be *admissible* if

(4,1) $$R \subseteq S$$

(4,2) $$aSb \rightarrow \xi a S \xi b$$

(4,3) $$cSa \wedge cSb \rightarrow cS(a \sqcap b)$$

(4,4) $$aSc \wedge bSc \rightarrow (a \sqcup b)Sc.$$

In a regular lattice group we have for every admissible quasi-order

(2″) $$(\xi a \sqcap \eta b) S (\xi b \sqcup \eta a).$$

This follows from (2′) and (4,1).

Now we shall represent the order of a regular lattice group (G, R) as a conjunction of admissible quasi-orders.

We denote binary relations in G, i.e., subsets of $G \times G$, by S with various indices; pairs of elements of G by $\alpha = (a_1, a_2)$, $\beta = (b_1, b_2)$, $\gamma = (c_1, c_2)$, and the statement $\neg\, a_1 S a_2$ by $\alpha \notin S$ or $a_1 \bar{S} a_2$.

Preliminary discussion

1) If $\gamma \notin S_1$, then $\gamma \notin S_1 \cap S_2 \cap \ldots$. Hence if we can find for every $\gamma \notin R$ a quasi-order $S^{(\gamma)}$ satisfying

(5) $$R \subseteq S^{(\gamma)} \wedge \gamma \notin S^{(\gamma)}$$

then

$$R = \bigcap_{\gamma \notin R} S^{(\gamma)}.$$

2) Presumably linear quasi-orders will be maximal quasi-orders. For if S is a non-linear quasi-order, then there exists a pair α with $a_1 \bar{S} a_2 \wedge a_2 \bar{S} a_1$; if we then add to S the pair (a_1, a_2) and at least all pairs that belong to it by virtue of monotony, that is, all pairs xa_1y, xa_2y, in other words, if we form the smallest quasi-order containing S and α, then we may expect to obtain a more extensive quasi-order.

So we search for maximal admissible quasi-orders with property (5). Such quasi-orders exist by the maximal principle; for if $c_1 \not\leqq c_2$, i.e., $\gamma \notin R$, then the set of admissible quasi-orders S with $\gamma \notin S$ is not empty; for R belong to it. Furthermore, every linearly ordered set (by inclusion $\subseteq$) of such quasi-orders has an upper bound, namely their union. This can be shown along the lines of the proof of Theorem 1 of § 2.5, page 165. Hence there exists a maximal quasi-order $S^{(\gamma)}$ with the property (5). The fact that it is maximal means

(6) $$S^{(\gamma)} \subseteq T \wedge \gamma \notin T \rightarrow S^{(\gamma)} = T$$

and $$S^{(\gamma)} \subset T \rightarrow \gamma \in T.$$

To prove that $S^{(\gamma)}$ is a *linear* quasi-order we proceed as follows: for an arbitrary admissible quasi-order S of G we define for every pair $\beta = (b_1, b_2)$ the relation S_β by

$$a_1 S_\beta a_2 \Leftrightarrow \bigwedge_{\xi, \eta} (\xi a_1 \sqcap \eta b_1) S (\xi a_2 \sqcup \eta b_2).$$

We claim that S_β is an admissible quasi-order.

(7,1) $$S \subseteq S_\beta.$$

Proof.

$$a_1 S a_2 \rightarrow \xi a_1 S \xi a_2 \qquad \text{by (4,2)}$$
$$\rightarrow (\xi a_1 \sqcap \eta b_1) S (\xi a_2 \sqcup \eta b_2).$$

(We have $(\xi a_1 \sqcap \eta b_1) R \xi a_1$, hence by (4,1) $(\xi a_1 \sqcap \eta b_1) S \xi a_1$.) This means among other things that $R \subseteq S_\beta$ and that S_β is reflexive.

(7,2) S_β is transitive: $a_1 S_\beta a_2 \wedge a_2 S_\beta a_3 \rightarrow a_1 S_\beta a_3$.

Proof. From $(\xi a_1 \sqcap \eta b_1)S(\xi a_2 \sqcup \eta b_2)$

and $(\xi a_2 \sqcap \eta b_1)S(\xi a_3 \sqcup \eta b_2)$

it follows that

$$(\xi a_1 \sqcap \eta b_1)S((\xi a_2 \sqcup \eta b_2) \sqcap \eta b_1) = (\xi a_2 \sqcap \eta b_1) \sqcup (\eta b_2 \sqcap \eta b_1)S((\xi a_3 \sqcup \eta b_2) \sqcup (\eta b_2 \sqcap \eta b_1)) = \xi a_3 \sqcup \eta b_2.$$

(7,3) $$a_1 S_\beta a_2 \to \zeta a_1 S_\beta \zeta a_2.$$

Proof. From $((\xi\zeta)a_1 \sqcap \eta b_1)S((\xi\zeta)a_2 \sqcup \eta b_2)$

it follows that $(\xi(\zeta a_1) \sqcup \eta b_1)S(\xi(\zeta a_2) \sqcup \eta b_2)$.

(7,4) $$aS_\beta a_1 \wedge aS_\beta a_2 \to aS_\beta(a_1 \sqcap a_2).$$

Proof. From $(\xi a \sqcap \eta b_1)S(\xi a_1 \sqcup \eta b_2)$

and $(\xi a \sqcap \eta b_1)S(\xi a_2 \sqcup \eta b_2)$

it follows that

$$(\xi a \sqcap \eta b_1)S((\xi a_1 \sqcup \eta b_2) \sqcap (\xi a_2 \sqcup \eta b_2)) = \xi(a_1 \sqcap a_2) \sqcup \eta b_2.$$

(7,5) $$a_1 S_\beta a \wedge a_2 S_\beta a \to (a_1 \sqcup a_2)S_\beta a.$$

The proof is dual to the preceding one.

So S_β is an admissible quasi-order of G.

Furthermore, we obviously have

(8) $$\alpha \in S_\beta \to \beta \in S_\alpha,$$

(9) $$\alpha \in S_\alpha \to \alpha \in S.$$

If we set $(a_2, a_1) = \alpha^{-1}$, then it follows from (2″) that

(10) $$\alpha^{-1} \in S_\alpha \quad \text{(for every } \alpha\text{)}.$$

Now we set $S^{(\gamma)} = S$ and construct S_γ. By (7,1)

$$S \subseteq S_\gamma.$$

Since $\gamma \notin S$, it follows from (9) that $\gamma \notin S_\gamma$. Hence from (6)

$$S^{(\gamma)} = S_\gamma.$$

Now it can be shown that $S^{(\gamma)} = S$ is a linear quasi-order: if $\alpha^{-1} \notin S$, then by (10) $S \neq S_\alpha$. But by (7,1) $S \subseteq S_\alpha$. Since S is maximal, it follows that $\gamma \in S_\alpha$ and now from (8) that $\alpha \in S_\gamma$.

The proof also holds for more general 'lattice domains'. (G, R, Ω) is called a *lattice domain* if (G, R) is a lattice and Ω a set of homomorphisms (which may be assumed to be a semigroup with unit element). A lattice domain is said to be *regular* if it is distributive and (2′) holds. A regular lattice domain can therefore be embedded in a direct product of linearly ordered lattice domains.

This includes the distributive lattices. They are lattice domains in which Ω consists of the unit element only, i.e., of the mapping $a \rightarrowtail a$. Then (2′) becomes

$$a \sqcap b \leqslant a \sqcup b$$

and this is always satisfied. Every distributive lattice can be embedded in a direct product of linearly ordered sets.[1]

[1] On this point we refer to the paper by P. Lorenzen, 'Teilbarkeitstheorie in Bereichen', which has already been mentioned on page 169, footnote 1; in particular to § 4.

Bibliography

Some fundamental papers

R. Dedekind, 'Über Zerlegungen von Zahlen durch ihren grössten gemeinsamen Teiler', *Festschrift Techn. Hochsch. Braunschweig*, 1897 und 'Ges. Werke', Bd. II, 103–147.

R. Dedekind, 'Über die von drei Moduln erzeugte Dualgruppe', *Math. Annalen* **53**, 1900, 371–403 und 'Ges. Werke', Bd. II, 236–271.

G. Birkhoff, 'On the combination of subalgebras', *Proc. Camb. Phil. Soc.* **29**, 1933, 441–464.

G. Birkhoff, 'On the structure of abstract algebras', *Proc. Camb. Phil. Soc.* **31**, 1935, 433–454.

J. Riguet, 'Relations binaires, fermetures et correspondences de Galois', *Bull. Soc. Math. France* **76**, 1948.

Monographs and textbooks

H. Hermes und G. Köthe, 'Die Theorie der Verbände', Enzykl. d. Math. Wiss., 2. Aufl., I. 1, 13, 1939.

G. Birkhoff, 'Lattice Theory', Amer. Math. Soc. Coll. Publications, Vol. XXV, 2nd ed., 1948.

M. L. Dubreil-Jacotin, L. Lesieur, R. Croisot, 'Leçons sur la théorie des treillis, des structures algébriques ordonnées et des treillis géométriques', Paris 1953.

H. Hermes, 'Einführung in die Verbandstheorie', Berlin, Göttingen, Heidelberg 1955.

Amer. Math. Soc., 'Proceedings in Pure Mathematics', Vol. II: Lattice Theory, 1961.

G. Szasz, 'Einführung in die Verbandstheorie', Budapest 1962.

Further references to literature can be found in most of the works quoted, particularly in Birkhoff, 'Lattice Theory', and in the last two works.

Index